The Writing Teacher's Toolbox

Forms, Checklists, and Charts
for Teaching Beginning Writers

by Carol Frank

Contributing Writer:
Connie Martin

Carson-Dellosa Publishing Company, Inc.
Greensboro, North Carolina

Dedication

to

Clint

Derek

Erik

Windy

Hailey

Celeste

And, an extra thank you to Celeste for providing some of the student samples.

Credits

Editor: Kelly Gunzenhauser

Layout Design: Jon Nawrocik

Cover Design: Peggy Jackson

Inside Illustrations: Bill Neville

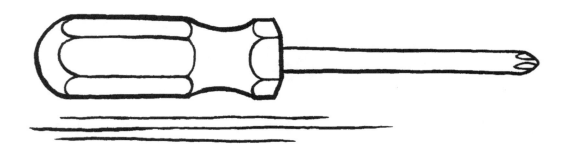

ISBN 0-88724-127-1

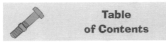

Introduction

Teachers love to talk. It just comes naturally. That's a good thing because we spend most of the day talking. It's the way we communicate with our students. Writing, on the other hand, may not be easy for some of us, and the thought that we must help students become proficient writers can be overwhelming. Where do we start? What do we teach? How do we assess? How is it possible to meet so many individual needs? Where do we find the time to add one more thing to the school day? Just remember that writing is simply another way to share what you have to say. There are many ways to share, and they are learned over a long period of time.

Children learn to write and become better writers by engaging in the process of writing every day. You will become a better writing teacher by teaching and modeling the process of writing every day. The goal is to offer students varied opportunities that encourage them to grow and become proficient writers. You are the driving force behind a successful writing program, and you must create an atmosphere that values each student as a writer, regardless of ability level. If children are viewed as writers, they will view themselves as writers. If you enjoy writing, your students will enjoy writing. It is most important for you to be a model of a person who enjoys writing, who shares writing and has a positive attitude toward it, and makes learning to write a fun experience. *The Writing Teacher's Toolbox: Forms, Checklists, and Charts for Teaching Beginning Writers* includes teaching strategies to help you build a program that teaches children to celebrate the joys of writing. In this book you will find the tools you need to:

- create an inviting atmosphere for writing
- understand and model the use of the writing process
- plan meaningful writing activities across the curriculum
- motivate students of all ability levels to become involved in the learning process
- encourage students' creativity
- conduct authentic assessment of student writing
- manage instruction and assessment
- become the "Best Writing Teacher" a student could have!

Children want to communicate. As students write, they discover the best ways to share what they have to say. When teachers, adults, and peers celebrate their achievements, they are encouraged to try new things. That is when real learning takes place and quality writing occurs. Celebrate their efforts as well as your own. You may decide you are, indeed, writers!

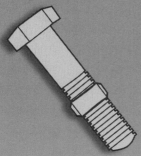

Chapter One
Reproducibles
Reproducibles
Reproducibles
Reproducibles

Balanced-Literacy Chart
(page 8)

Writer's-Workshop Schedule
(page 17)

Mini-Lesson Record
(page 22)

Status-of-the-Class Checklist
(page 23)

Writing in a Balanced-Literacy Classroom

Children learn at different rates and have various writing abilities. They come to school writing at different developmental stages depending on their maturity levels, as well as past exposure to and experiences with writing. Some will be capable of complex writing while others are just beginning to communicate in written form. You may have a kindergarten student who is ready for simple story writing, while a third grade teacher may have several students for whom English is a second language. Those older students may be working for a period of time simply to understand the conventions of written and spoken English. You will need to continually assess needs, analyze abilities, and plan instruction for students at all levels. Fortunately, lessons geared for a balanced-literacy classroom allow for that type of ongoing assessment and planning.

In a balanced-literacy classroom, daily lessons are designed to guide students to read, write, speak, listen, and observe in a variety of whole-group, small-group, and independent work settings. All are equally important communication skills. Reading and writing are so connected that they even share many of the same descriptors: read aloud and write aloud, Shared Reading and Shared Writing, Guided Reading and Guided Writing, and Independent Reading and Independent Writing. The types of writing that are evident in a balanced-literacy classroom are designed to allow teachers to experience and share writing *TO* children, as well as *WITH* children. These experiences are *BRIDGED* by guided writing, so that writing *BY* children and *FOR* children can take place. The graphic organizer that follows shows the similarities between reading and writing activities in a balanced-literacy classroom.

© Carson-Dellosa

BALANCED-LITERACY CHART

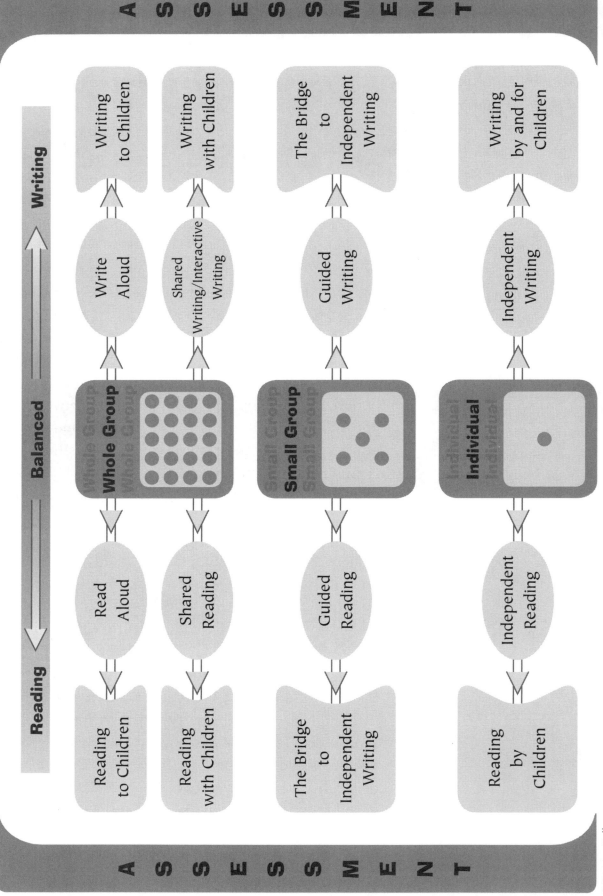

Reading

Balanced

Writing

	Reading		Writing	
Whole Group	Reading to Children	Read Aloud	Write Aloud	Writing to Children
	Reading with Children	Shared Reading	Shared Writing/Interactive Writing	Writing with Children
Small Group	The Bridge to Independent Writing	Guided Reading	Guided Writing	The Bridge to Independent Writing
Individual	Reading by Children	Independent Reading	Independent Writing	Writing by and for Children

ASSESSMENT

ASSESSMENT

The Writing Teacher's Toolbox • CD-0354

Writing Aloud

Writing TO Children

Writing TO children can take place on large chart paper, an overhead projector, or on the chalkboard. It can be done as a whole-group or small-group activity. In this activity, you model how to write and how to think about what you write. Your role is to compose text. The students' role is to observe the writing process. Write and talk out loud about what is being written. Verbalize why it is being written as you record. For example, you might say, "I will start my next sentence with a capital letter because every sentence starts with a capital letter." Or, "I'll need to underline *Charlotte's Web* because it is the title of a book." Targeted skills might include the conventions used, such as punctuation, handwriting, spacing of words, spelling, and vocabulary. For older students, target skills appropriate for the grade level, such as the inclusion of descriptive words, action words, compounds, quotation marks, and abbreviations.

A Writing-Aloud Activity to Try: Morning Message

Designate a special area to record and display the morning message. Write a message to students about the day's schedule, lunch choices, or something special that will be happening. After you have written the message and discussed its meaning with the class, choose students to locate specific items in the message, such as words with short "a" sound, nouns, two-syllable words, etc., depending on the skill(s) you are targeting. Make the activity multilevel by choosing students to locate specific items according to their ability levels. For example, if you know that Mia can locate a capital letter and Lana can locate a personal pronoun, have them point out these features in the writing. Leave the message in place during the day for students to review as they wish. Refer to page 10 for examples of morning messages you may choose to write.

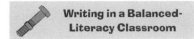

Morning Message Example #1

> September 5
>
> Dear Boys and Girls,
>
>
> Good morning! Today is Monday.
> We have music today. We will sing and have fun.
>
>
> Love,
> Mrs. Duncan

Morning Message Example #2

> October 5
>
> Dear Students,
>
>
> Good morning! Today in social studies we will discuss wants and needs. I want a new car, but do I need one? What do you need? What do you want? What is the difference? Make a list of five things you believe you need and five things you want. Be ready to discuss the items on your lists and your reasons for including each.
>
>
> Sincerely,
> Mrs. Duncan

Shared Writing

Writing WITH Children 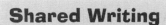 Shared Writing is an easy way to create a positive, cooperative writing environment that models purposes for writing and how writing works (for example, the correct conventions for getting ideas onto paper). In a Shared-Writing activity, you act as the recorder while modeling good writing behaviors and introducing new skills, such as brainstorming, narrowing a topic, word selection, spelling, punctuation, grammar, etc. It is the time for you to construct a piece of writing with students. Your role during Shared Writing is to help children compose and record the text. The students' role is to help compose the text to be written. Have students share ideas as you record them on chart paper, the chalkboard, or the overhead projector. Writing them gives students an opportunity to see their ideas. During a Shared-Writing activity, take dictation from students and discuss with them the choices of words to use, meanings they are trying to convey, and the correct conventions to consider. Then, make a joint decision about what to include in the writing.

Writing-Aloud Activities to Try:
There are many opportunities to share writing experiences with students. Consider these.
- Write about field trips, visitors, and other activities you experience together.
- Hold class meetings on a regular basis. After a meeting, discuss the most important ideas. Let students tell you what they want you to write. Display the minutes in the classroom for easy reference.
- Read a piece of literature aloud. Write students' feelings about the literature that was shared.
- Create a list of classroom rules, rewards, and consequences.
- Write class observations about a science experiment.
- Develop a new ending (or two) to a well-known story.
- Write together about the Student of the Week.

If you write on chart paper, use clothespins to attach the finished writing to a coat hanger, then place it in an area of the classroom for children to reference. Selections may also be bound to create a big book called *Our Class Field Trips*, which can be added to the reading center. Students love to read these again and again.

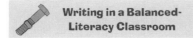

Interactive Writing

Writing WITH Children Interactive Writing is similar to Shared Writing except that students actually help record text. You and your students compose and record text together and "share" the pen/pencil. This activity works best in small groups so each student has an opportunity to record text on the chart. Each student in the group should have pencil and paper, a dry erase board, or a chalkboard to assure participation while they are waiting to record text on the chart. Your role is to coach students to do as much of the actual writing as they can.

Before-, During- and After-Writing Activities to Try:

Before writing: Have a class discussion to choose a topic. The writing should have purpose and meaning for students. They can plan to write about a class event, a thematic topic, morning news, or anything that is important to them. (The example on page 13 is about a trip to the zoo.)

During writing: You may want to use lined chart paper for this activity. Fold a piece of chart paper in half to create upper and lower portions. Reopen the paper and place it on an easel or attach it so that students can reach it comfortably while recording text. Decide on the first sentence with student input. If there are questions about any part of the writing, use the upper portion of the chart to model as students discuss letters, words, and sentences they are writing. In the student-written example on page 13, the student has investigated the spelling of homonyms (to, two, and too), the formation of a letter (capital versus lowercase w), and correct punctuation (!). On the lower portion of the chart, compose the text by writing each word the group chooses. Have students take turns writing a portion of the text on the chart (usually just a word or two, depending on ability level). As students write, act as a facilitator by prompting students to think about the letters, words, and conventions needed to compose the text. When complete, the text is usually a few sentences in length. To complete a longer piece of writing, schedule another session.

After writing: Place the chart paper in an area of the classroom where it will be available for students to reference in the future as you review spelling, conventions, word patterns, and any other strategies addressed during an Interactive-Writing session. Interactive Writing can be planned for use with students during the time set aside for Shared or Guided Writing.

to two too

monkey

hw   g

!

We went to the
zoo. We saw a
monkey and a tiger.
It was fun!

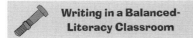

Guided Writing (The Bridge to Independent Writing)

Writing BY and FOR Children

Just as the name implies, Guided Writing occurs when a student composes text with your guidance and encouragement. This is where you work with an individual, a small group, or the whole group as needed to teach skills that will guide each student to become a more proficient writer. Your role is to support the task of writing, revising, and editing text. The students write, revise, and edit text with your support. To keep topics current, continually assess each student's progress and devise short lessons to meet needs as they arise. For example, you notice that several students have difficulty sticking to a topic, so you have a small-group lesson in which those students share what has been written and decide if all details relate to the topic. If one student is trying to add dialogue, help him understand when to use quotation marks. And, if every student in the class keeps using the tired, old word "said," have a whole-group lesson and brainstorm better words for "said" such as "whispered," "chuckled," "yelled," "begged," or "whimpered." Display this word chart in the room for students to reference as they write.

Guided Writing Steps to Follow:
- Provide support as students develop writing pieces.
- Provide encouragement as students see other pieces of work that classmates have developed through the writing process.
- Encourage classmates to support each other's writing efforts.
- Allow students to share ideas in a risk-free environment where all ideas are respected.
- Allow each student to work at her own pace and develop from her own starting point.
- Guide students to develop fluency in writing and become independent writers.

Independent Writing

Writing BY and FOR Children

Independent Writers can write without teacher involvement. These students seek opportunities to write and work their way through the writing process on their own. They write, revise, and edit text without your assistance, seeking feedback as needed. As students become Independent Writers, they use their writing skills to help them think about the things they are learning in literature, math, social studies, and science. They write their own interpretations of the observations they make. They write notes and lists. They record observations. They note connections between the things they learn and the real world. They organize written information. They write down questions that arise during the day. They reflect on learning, then use writing as a way to present their learning and information to others in the form of reports and publications. They support and encourage each other as writers. In short, Independent Writers use the skills and strategies that you have modeled for them daily.

This is the part of writing during which students think about learning and use writing skills to organize that learning independently. Your role is to support the efforts of students. Of course, the length and complexity of the writing will vary depending on each student's ability level. Matthew may write a one-page report while Zach creates an entire research paper based on a given topic. The important thing to remember is that each student is independently creating a piece of writing in order to share his learning with others.

You can provide many opportunities for students to practice Independent Writing. Journal writing is a good place to start. Entries are usually short, so students don't feel overwhelmed. You can find entire books to help teach journal writing, because there are so many ways to write in a journal. Below are two kinds to get you started. For more ideas, refer to Chapter 8 (page 92).

Two Types of Journal Writing:
A personal journal is a notebook somewhat like a diary. Students write at regular journal times that you establish. You may begin by including journal writing for five minutes once each week, then work up to writing 15 minutes daily. Students usually write about whatever they choose, and you may or may not assess the writing. The goal is to encourage students to feel comfortable expressing themselves in written form. Store journals where students can easily access them, perhaps at their desks or in a writing center. If journals are stored in a writing center, choose a student to pass out journals at writing time, then collect and return them to their place of storage. You may occasionally invite students to write notes directed to you in their journals, then collect the journals, read each note, and respond in writing to each student.

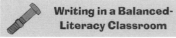 

In response logs or learning logs, students record their reactions to the things they are learning in reading, science, social studies, and math. They may even have a different journal for each subject. Students may sometimes record their reflections about a lesson, stating what they learned or writing questions about materials that need further explanation. At other times, they may write in response to a question or prompt that you have posed.

Example 1: You teach a math lesson on two-digit multiplication. You want to know which students really understand the process. Ask students to write out the steps to a selected two-digit multiplication problem, explaining what they are thinking during each step. This is a great way to have students reflect on a process, think about the steps in order, and practice using clear language in order to write an explanation of the process.

Example 2: Students read two stories by the same author. Have them compare the main character from each story, decide which character they like best, and explain why.

Your next step is to review these journals, assess student progress, and note who needs further instruction. For example, after reading journals, you may realize that Suzie and Addie need to review two-digit multiplication, and that Seth understands the concept of comparison.

Writer's Workshop

All Types of Writing

Students need opportunities to experience and explore each type of writing from Writing Aloud to Independent Writing. The challenge is to find time during the school day to include them all. How will you manage this fine trick along with everything else you are supposed to do? Fortunately, there is a wonderful organizational format for writing called Writer's Workshop.

The purpose of Writer's Workshop is to allow students uninterrupted, independent writing time following a model and a schedule. Writer's Workshop lasts about an hour. It is broken into segments of time designated for specific writing purposes. Shorten the times for sessions as needed when students become familiar with the process. Whether a student writes a one-page report or creates a research paper based on a given topic, remember that each student is independently creating a piece of writing in order to share his learning with others. For more information, refer to the bibliography on page 128. The following illustration is a model for scheduling a Writer's Workshop session.

WRITER'S-WORKSHOP SCHEDULE

For the week of:

Modeled-Writing Mini-Lesson	Status of the Class	Writing Activity	Sharing
10-15 minutes	**2-3 minutes**	**30 minutes**	**5-10 minutes**
Model while thinking aloud. Students observe, then participate. Use a short, focused activity that targets one skill based on students' needs. Incorporate good literature, if desired. Reference classroom resources.	Determine which stage of the writing process each student is engaged in as well as the amount of support needed from you or peers.	Students write. You write. Students are involved in planning, working on drafts, revising, editing, or publishing. Conduct individual or group conferences. Students may share drafts with peers for feedback.	Students may share in large or small groups. Students may share unfinished pieces of writing for feedback. Some students may share finished pieces. Other students listen, question, or retell.

Entire Exercise 47-58 Minutes

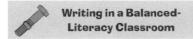

Summary of Writer's-Workshop Activities

Writer's-Workshop Activity #1: Mini-Lesson, Whole Group (10-15 minutes)

Have students gather in a designated area of the classroom, if possible. Make sure that all students are involved and focused because the mini-lesson is where skills are introduced and students observe as you model thinking and writing. Some teachers ask students to come to a carpet, others have them sit at writing tables, and others keep students at their desks for instruction during the mini-lesson (you can choose to push desks together in a circle). You may use the chalkboard, overhead projector, or chart paper for writing. The goals are to set the stage for students to become excited about writing and to help them understand that they can use writing as a tool to share what they want to say. Make it clear that, although people express themselves differently, all ideas will be respected.

The importance of the mini-lesson cannot be stressed enough. This is the time when students watch you, the writer, expressing your thoughts as you move through each step in the process of creating a piece of writing to share. Let students see you as a writer. Sharing samples of your own writing with students is a must. If you find it difficult to write in front of an audience, try writing a short piece you can practice at home the night before. Remember, students need to hear your thought process as you write.

Base lessons on skills that you have determined students are ready to learn. A mini-lesson can be anything from how to choose a topic or add descriptive details, to how to edit a piece for spelling and grammar. The most effective mini-lessons are short, are focused on one skill at a time, and are tailored to meet student needs. The Mini-Lesson Record on page 22 can be used to plan and record information about the mini-lessons you present.

Writer's-Workshop Activity #2: Status of the Class (2-3 minutes)

Touch base with each student to be sure everyone has a plan for working during the Independent-Writing time ahead. It may be as simple as having each student tell you her writing topic. A Status-of-the-Class session lets you see who is ready to work and who needs more guidance before beginning to write independently. If you wish, you can record plans on a chart or on the overhead to help you track students' progress as they move through the writing process. The Status-of-the-Class Checklist on page 23 can be used to help you keep track of which students have met with you and still need to discuss their writing.

Writer's-Workshop Activity #3: Writing/Process Writing/Independent Writing (30 minutes)

Have students write, using the skills and strategies you have modeled. Also, ask them to read and discuss each other's writing. As they are working, hold individual and small-group conferences as needed. Conferences may be scheduled or impromptu. During a conference, you can assess a student's level of development or provide guidance regarding a particular skill. At all times, provide encouragement to write as well as support for using modeled skills to write. Even though students are working on different writing activities, they will be following the stages of the writing process. These stages are prewriting, drafting, revising, editing, and publishing. Each stage will be discussed in detail later in this book. During this time, make sure to leave a few minutes to engage in your own writing. Students need to see that writing is important to you. Always model what you expect students to do.

Writer's-Workshop Activity #4: Share Time (5-10 minutes)

Select students to share writing. Some students will volunteer daily. Others may need more time and encouragement before feeling comfortable sharing their writing with peers who listen, question, and reflect. To build a friendly environment for sharing, have students make two positive statements about each shared piece of writing before making comments or asking questions.

You may begin the next Writer's-Workshop session by sharing your writing and asking for opinions about things such as how to add more detail to make it more interesting. The key is sharing what you have written with students. As the year progresses they can see firsthand the steps in the writing process.

Sample Writer's-Workshop Activities

Sample Mini-Lesson, Whole Group (10-15 minutes)
Skill: How to Choose a Topic for Writing

Decide if you will use the chalkboard, chart paper, or an overhead projector. Gather students for a mini-lesson. Begin by saying, "If I wanted to tell you about something I did with my family last weekend, I could write about having a cookout, going to a baseball game, buying a new car, or washing my dog." List all four choices as you name them.

Then, continue the conversation, "Which one do I want to write about? Which one do I remember the best? Hmm—I think I'll tell about washing my dog. That will be the topic of my writing. The topic means the main thing I am writing about." (This is the topic that you practiced at home!)

Quickly plan your writing by sketching a picture and writing a few ideas for students to see. "Here is my dog, Ralph. Now, what can I tell about washing him? I can tell about getting him in the tub, I can tell about what he did with the soap, and I can tell what he did when we were drying him off. Now, I'm ready to write." At this point, students should know your purpose for writing.

Write quickly for a few minutes. Let students see what you are writing, but write without reading it aloud as you write. Let students also see that you take your time, you may cross things out and change them, and that the writing you are doing is getting ideas on paper. When you have written several sentences, say, "I don't have time to finish my writing now, but I'll continue to work on it while you are writing. Think about everything you did last weekend. Write three of those things down, then choose one to tell us about in your writing. Before you write, draw a picture and list some words to help you think about what you want to say about your topic. You may not finish today, but we will work on these again tomorrow during writing time." Continue with your writing while students work.

cookout
ball game
new car
washing dog

Ralph
tub
soap
dry

Sample Status-of-the-Class Activity (2-3 minutes)
Skill: How to Choose a Topic for Writing

After the mini-lesson, walk around and talk to each student about his topic. "Take a minute to consider, then be ready to tell me the three things you are going to think about before you choose a topic. Then, you may begin." You should already have rules in place about where and how to get writing supplies so that the transition between the mini-lesson and the writing time goes smoothly.

Sample Writing/Process-Writing/Independent Writing Activity (30 minutes)
Skill: How to Choose a Topic for Writing

Students choose a topic, then draw and write a few words to plan their writing. They begin to write sentences about the topic. Some students will only be able to draw a picture and write a few words, while others may write several paragraphs, depending on ability. Monitor students by helping them choose ideas, sound out words for spelling, or simply encouraging them to share what they want to say in the way that is best for them. Take a few minutes to continue writing the piece you began in the mini-lesson. Let students know it is your writing time, too, and they should work without you for a short time.

STATUS-OF-THE-CLASS CHECKLIST

For the week of: October 17

Student Name	Monday	Tuesday	Wednesday	Thursday	Friday
Anthony	P	D	D	PC	TC
Ashley	PC	TC	P	P	D
Brandon	D	D	D	PC	TC
Daysha	SR	P	P	D	TC
Delaney	P	D	PC	TC	SR
Diandre	P	P	D	PC	TC
Erik	D	D	PC	PC	TC
Hannah	SR	P	D	D	PC
Jacob	TC	PC	SR	P	P
Jeremy	P	D	D	TC	PC
Jessica	D	PC	TC	SR	P
Juan	P	P	D	D	SR
Kelsey	SR	D	TC	PC	P
Kiara	P	P	D	D	PC
Lamar	D	PC	TC	SR	SR
Maria	P	TC	PC	PC	SR
Marvin	D	D	TC	PC	P
Megan	TC	SR	P	P	D
Patrick	PC	P	P	D	D
Shane	D	P	P	TC	PC
Stephanie	SR	D	D	P	PC
Tia	TC	SR	P	D	D
Trent	P	P	D	D	PC
Whitney	D	D	PC	TC	SR
Zach	P	D	D	PC	TC

Key   P = Planning, D = Draft, PC = Peer Conference, TC = Teacher Conference, SR = Self-Reflection

Sample Share-Time Activity (5-10 minutes)
Skill: How to Choose a Topic for Writing

Begin by asking students, "Who would like to tell us what you did last weekend? We'll choose just a couple of people today, but others can share during writing time tomorrow. Remember, we all write differently, and as listeners, we want to think of two good things we can say about each person's writing. Also, think about a question you could ask the writer to find out more." Allow students to do this as a whole group, or when students are used to the process, you may wish to let them work in small groups.

Date	Topic	Comments

STATUS-OF-THE-CLASS CHECKLIST

For the week of:

Student Name	Monday	Tuesday	Wednesday	Thursday	Friday

Key | P = Planning, D = Draft, PC = Peer Conference, TC = Teacher Conference, SR = Self-Reflection

Assessing and Maintaining Writing

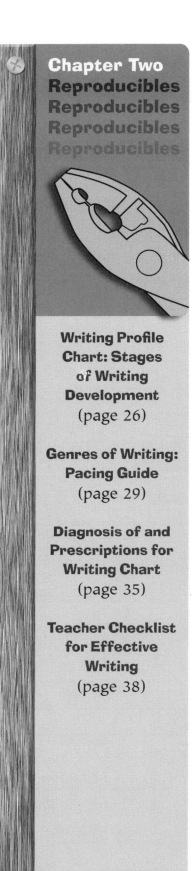

When you enter an elementary classroom, you find a variety of written expression. There may be scribbling, random marks, pictures to represent words, strings of letters, words, phrases, sentence fragments, and even complete sentences grouped together to make stories. To create an instructional program that meets the needs of each child in the class, you must be aware of the developmental stages of writing and identify the stage at which each student is performing. The pages that follow show the stages of writing with descriptors (benchmarks) of each stage and samples of what writing looks like at each stage. The grade level and approximate age are also included. Note that some students, particularly those for whom English is a second language, may be chronologically older, yet show characteristics of beginning writers.

Over the last several years, there have been a variety of titles for the five developmental stages of writing. The important parts to understand are the descriptors of each stage so that you can assess students' work and plan instruction to help them grow as writers. The titles used in this book for the five developmental stages of writing are:

- early emergent (also labeled as prewriter, preemergent, or scribble stage)
- emergent (also labeled as novice or isolated-letter stage)
- developing (also labeled as apprentice or transitional)
- early independent (also labeled as capable, proficient, or stylized)
- independent (also labeled as experienced, distinguished, fluent, or at the writing stage)

These descriptors provide a basis for student assessment. You can use them to determine needs, then place students with similar needs in small groups and plan mini-lessons to address those needs. The Writing Profile Chart: Stages of Writing Development reproducible on page 26 can be used to document assessment. Take samples of student writing. Staple a copy of the sheet to each student's writing sample. Assess each student's developmental level and mark it on the sheet. Date the assessed writing samples and place them in the students' writing files or portfolios. Continue this procedure throughout the year as documentation of student progress.

Finally, note that these benchmarks will vary from state to state, and even from district to district. They will also change as research and educational trends change. The benchmarks and descriptors in this book were compiled from various states, such as North Carolina, New York, and Indiana.

Assessing and Maintaining Writing

WRITING PROFILE CHART: STAGES OF WRITING DEVELOPMENT

Early Emergent	Emergent	Developing	Early Independent	Independent
3-5 years prekindergarten	4-6 years kindergarten	5-7 years first grade	6-8 years second grade	7-9 years third grade
[ ] Draws pictures to express ideas and information, and conveys meaning effectively [ ] Dictates captions or stories to describe or give information about pictures [ ] Uses scribble writing or random lines [ ] Uses letters and letter-like symbols to write first and/or last name [ ] May use some letters to represent ideas (letter strings) [ ] Can tell one or two sentences before writing a story (talking helps organize thoughts for writing) [ ] Takes risks and attempts writing [ ] Can tell about own writing to others	[ ] Dictates sentences to be written (simple directions, descriptions, and stories) [ ] Begins to use spacing [ ] Makes an attempt to write [ ] Conveys ideas using pictures and symbols [ ] Uses left-to-right progress (writes from left to right and top to bottom) [ ] Uses temporary spelling according to beginning sounds heard and letter names [ ] Uses initial and final consonant sounds to spell words. Begins to place vowels correctly within words. [ ] Copies words from environment. Spells some familiar words correctly. [ ] Writes one or two thoughts or ideas to begin to focus on a theme or topic [ ] Reads and shares own writing with others	☑ Writes using whole words (consonants and short vowels) ☑ Puts spaces between words ☑ Writes simple sentences that make sense ☑ Attempts to use capital letters (beginnings of sentences, proper names, I) ☑ Uses punctuation in the writing (periods, question marks) ☑ Puts words together in a sentence format. Relates short sentences to a topic and stays focused. ☑ Writes in logical sequences ☑ Selects writing topics. Varies writing (stories, poems, lists, letters, journal entries). ☑ Rereads sentences to predict and check words ☑ Spells some high-frequency words correctly. Writes known words fluently. ☑ Records sounds in sequence. Uses temporary spelling. ☑ Takes risks in writing ☑ Uses short patterns or repetitive sentences. Uses models to help with writing (structured writing). ☑ Begins to revise and add to writing in response to questions. Uses some detail which may be presented in list form. ☑ Tells a story or reads writing to others. Publishes work with support. ☑ Begins to reflect on own writing (with guidance) ☑ Maintains a writing portfolio/notebook	[ ] Uses a prewriting activity to plan for writing [ ] Shows evidence of appropriate capitalization, punctuation, and spacing [ ] Uses a strong, fluent, writing vocabulary [ ] Varies sentence patterns, structure, and length [ ] Uses some temporary spelling to keep ideas flowing, but uses more standard spelling with previously taught words [ ] Writes in a variety of genres [ ] Begins to consider audience and purpose (writes descriptive stories, narratives, persuasive stories, and informal passages) [ ] Generates a good story independently, using characters, settings, and events [ ] Develops ideas sequentially [ ] Stays focused on a topic [ ] Edits for punctuation, grammar, and spelling [ ] Checks writing by reading aloud [ ] Publishes writing [ ] Reflects on own writing (with guidance) recognizing strengths and weaknesses [ ] Maintains a writing portfolio/notebook	[ ] Considers purpose and audience for writing [ ] Plans story using prewriting (unassisted) [ ] Organizes and writes sentences and stories that have clear beginnings and ends [ ] Varies the ways sentences begin [ ] Connects related ideas by using paragraphs to organize information [ ] Shows originality of word selection by use of interesting language and strong verbs [ ] Uses more conventions than temporary spelling. Spells most words correctly. [ ] Uses standard application of mechanics (periods, quotation marks, commas, and question marks) [ ] Initiates revisions to clarify,

> My Favorite Person is
> My Daddy. Bcos he Buy
> Me a Boib Dolls and He
> Takes Me To The Mall.
> I like him verymuch. We
> Do Fun thins. MY
> Daddy Plais With me.

WRITING PROFILE CHART: STAGES OF WRITING DEVELOPMENT

Assessing and Maintaining Writing	Early Emergent Early Emergent Early Emergent 3-5 years prekindergarten	Emergent Emergent Emergent 4-6 years kindergarten	Developing Developing Developing 5-7 years first grade	Early Independent Early Independent Early Independent 6-8 years second grade	Independent Independent Independent 7-9 years third grade
	[ ] Draws pictures to express ideas and information, and conveys meaning effectively [ ] Dictates captions or stories to describe or give information about pictures [ ] Uses scribble writing or random lines [ ] Uses letters and letter-like symbols to write first and/or last name [ ] May use some letters to represent ideas (letter strings) [ ] Can tell one or two sentences before writing a story (talking helps organize thoughts for writing) [ ] Takes risks and attempts writing [ ] Can tell about own writing to others	[ ] Dictates sentences to be written (simple directions, descriptions, and stories) [ ] Begins to use spacing [ ] Makes an attempt to write [ ] Conveys ideas using pictures and symbols [ ] Uses left-to-right progress (writes from left to right and top to bottom) [ ] Uses temporary spelling according to beginning sounds heard and letter names [ ] Uses initial and final consonant sounds to spell words. Begins to place vowels correctly within words. [ ] Copies words from environment. Spells some familiar words correctly. [ ] Writes one or two thoughts or ideas to begin to focus on a theme or topic [ ] Reads and shares own writing with others	[ ] Writes using whole words (consonants and short vowels) [ ] Puts spaces between words [ ] Writes simple sentences that make sense [ ] Attempts to use capital letters (beginnings of sentences, proper names, I) [ ] Uses punctuation in the writing (periods, question marks) [ ] Puts words together in a sentence format. Relates short sentences to a topic and stays focused. [ ] Writes in logical sequences [ ] Selects writing topics. Varies writing (stories, poems, lists, letters, journal entries). [ ] Rereads sentences to predict and check words [ ] Spells some high-frequency words correctly. Writes known words fluently. [ ] Records sounds in sequence. Uses temporary spelling. [ ] Takes risks in writing [ ] Uses short patterns or repetitive sentences. Uses models to help with writing (structured writing). [ ] Begins to revise and add to writing in response to questions. Uses some detail which may be presented in list form. [ ] Tells a story or reads writing to others. Publishes work with support. [ ] Begins to reflect on own writing (with guidance) [ ] Maintains a writing portfolio/notebook	[ ] Uses a prewriting activity to plan for writing [ ] Shows evidence of appropriate capitalization, punctuation, and spacing [ ] Uses a strong, fluent, writing vocabulary [ ] Varies sentence patterns, structure, and length [ ] Uses some temporary spelling to keep ideas flowing, but uses more standard spelling with previously taught words [ ] Writes in a variety of genres [ ] Begins to consider audience and purpose (writes descriptive stories, narratives, persuasive stories, and informal passages) [ ] Generates a good story independently, using characters, settings, and events [ ] Develops ideas sequentially [ ] Stays focused on a topic [ ] Edits for punctuation, grammar, and spelling [ ] Checks writing by reading aloud [ ] Publishes writing [ ] Reflects on own writing (with guidance) recognizing strengths and weaknesses [ ] Maintains a writing portfolio/notebook	[ ] Considers purpose and audience for writing [ ] Plans story using prewriting (unassisted) [ ] Organizes and writes sentences and stories that have clear beginnings and ends [ ] Varies the ways sentences begin [ ] Connects related ideas by using paragraphs to organize information [ ] Shows originality of word selection by use of interesting language and strong verbs [ ] Uses more conventions than temporary spelling. Spells most words correctly. [ ] Uses standard application of mechanics (periods, quotation marks, commas, and question marks) [ ] Initiates revisions to clarify, express ideas, and add detail [ ] Initiates editing own writing for mechanics, grammar, and spelling [ ] Publishes completed writing and shares with others [ ] Reflects on own writing and sets goals to improve [ ] Maintains a writing portfolio/notebook

Assessing and Maintaining Writing	Early Emergent Early Emergent Early Emergent	Emergent Emergent Emergent	Developing Developing Developing	Early Independent Early Independent Early Independent	Independent Independent Independent
	3–5 years prekindergarten	4–6 years kindergarten	5–7 years first grade	6–8 years second grade	7–9 years third grade

3–5 years prekindergarten

writing sample:

(It is yellow, brown, blue and yellow.)

(Dear Mom)

(We can go to Mimi's for dinner tomorrow.)

ΠOBEOLEN
I see a snowman.

4–6 years kindergarten

writing sample:

I Wi'Sh I had SHU.
I NWLO PUNO.
I WYLO RAKе leus.

WRHICL

WE ARE HAUING A CAROIVAL.

5–7 years first grade

writing sample:

My Favorite Person is
My Daddy. Bcos he Buy
Me a BaibDolls and He
Takes Me To The Mall.
I like him verymuch. We
Do Fun things. MY
Daddy Plais Withe Me.

6–8 years second grade

writing sample:

My Magic Rock

One day my friend and I went to
the park. We were walking on the
sand and I felt something under
my feet. It was a rock of many
colors. When I held it in my
hand it started talking. "I am a
magic rock," it said. "Make a wish
and I will grant it." "I wish I
could dance forever."

I have not stopped dancing since
that surprising day in the park.

7–9 years third grade

writing sample:

My Trip to New York

Last year I went to New
york with my mom and daddy.
We had alot of fun together. I
saw a lot of my friends and we
played sports together.

We played basketball and
baseball. Then we played
soccer. My team won when we
played basketball and baseball.

I hope to go back to New
York someday. I want to play
more sports with my friends.

Disney World

My family and I went to Disney World.
My three aunts, three cousins, my brother,
my mommy, my grandma, and I were very
excited! This was our first trip to Disney
World in Florida.

First, we rode the Dumbo ride. We got in
the elephant and spun around in circles.
Next, we rode the merry-go-round. It
had lots of different horses bobbing up
and down. I chose the white one. Then we
went to the cowboy's place and saw lots of
cowboy hats and guns. Our next stop was
the train roller coaster. I didn't want to ride
it because I was scared. The train went in
to the dark mountains and came out three
times. The next ride was the water roller
coaster. I didn't want to go on that one
either. We went up slowly and came down
really fast! The bumper cars were our last
ride. I bumped my brother and my cousins.

At sunset, my whole fmily was tired. We
piled into our white mini-van and returned
to my great-grandma's house. I think
everyone would enjoy a trip to Disney
World. I know I did!

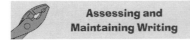

Genres of Writing

Students write for a variety of reasons and for different audiences. They are exposed to the process of writing through your modeling. They develop the characteristics of writers by sharing, responding to, and publishing their writing in an environment where all attempts are respected.

Most writing curriculums are spiraling, meaning that students will revisit skills on many occasions during the course of a school year, but more in-depth each time. Skills are not learned sequentially or in a linear manner. Your district may have a writing curriculum for you to follow as you plan writing instruction throughout the year, or you may wish to use the Genres of Writing Pacing Guide (page 29). This guide is compatible with most writing curriculums and provides suggestions for introducing different types, or genres, of writing. The guide is blocked into six-week intervals. Genres and skills from one block may be introduced or reinforced during any of the intervals and used according to local/state objectives. Once the genre or skill has been introduced, continue to provide students with opportunities to practice writing it throughout the entire school year.

By focusing on these specific genres, students have the opportunity to build a strong continuum of writing skills. Listed under each genre on the Genres of Writing Pacing Guide (page 29) are many suggested forms of writing that will appeal to young writers. Give your students a chance to try as many writing formats as possible!

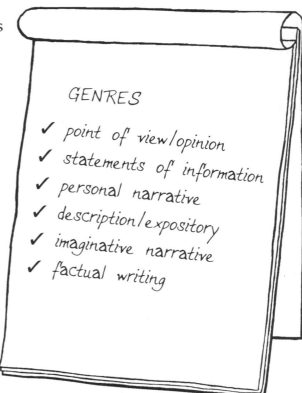

GENRES
✓ point of view/opinion
✓ statements of information
✓ personal narrative
✓ description/expository
✓ imaginative narrative
✓ factual writing

GENRES OF WRITING: PACING GUIDE

Assessing and Maintaining Writing	Statements of Information	Description (Expository)	Personal Narrative	Point of View/Opinion	Imaginative Narrative	Factual Writing
	August/September approximately six-week intervals	**October/November** approximately six-week intervals	**December/January** approximately six-week intervals	**February** approximately six-week intervals	**March/April** approximately six-week intervals	**May/June** approximately six-week intervals
	[ ] Lists [ ] Simple instructions [ ] Directions to complete a task [ ] News of the day [ ] Captions [ ] Journal entries [ ] Signs [ ] Class rules and consequences [ ] Charts [ ] Calendars [ ] Cards/notes/letters [ ] Messages [ ] Message boards [ ] Menus [ ] Labels [ ] Telephone numbers [ ] Invitations [ ] Addresses [ ] Retelling of new information [ ] Books [ ] Notices for school/class activities [ ] How-to booklets [ ] Memos [ ] Brochures [ ] Newspapers [ ] Recipes [ ] Posters [ ] Advertisements/want ads [ ] Commercials	[ ] Explain an idea [ ] Explain information [ ] Use words and pictures [ ] Tell about a person or character [ ] Tell about a place [ ] Tell about an object [ ] Respond and elaborate (who, what, where, when, why, how) [ ] Advertisements [ ] Comparison (Venn diagram) [ ] Contrast (Venn diagram) [ ] Brochures [ ] Captions [ ] Labels [ ] Posters [ ] Observation journals [ ] Poetry	[ ] Everyone has a "How-to" tale [ ] Reading stories [ ] Reading autobiographies [ ] Write to tell experiences [ ] Books [ ] Stories [ ] Summaries [ ] Conversations	[ ] Short stories [ ] Journal entries [ ] Personal letters [ ] Book reviews [ ] Evaluation of books and activities like movies, products, restaurants, etc. [ ] Reflections [ ] Explaining word problems in math [ ] Responses to stories or poems [ ] Poems	[ ] A story to tell [ ] Author's craft [ ] Sense of story/story maps [ ] Sequence events [ ] Journal or response log entries [ ] Respond to text read by writing and retelling [ ] Report cards [ ] Venn diagrams [ ] Written queues [ ] Posters [ ] Written conversations [ ] Flowcharts/time lines [ ] News articles [ ] Interactive journals [ ] Books [ ] Plays/scripts [ ] Stories [ ] Songs [ ] Poetry	[ ] Research: books, magazines, encyclopedias, dictionaries, etc. [ ] Predicts and explains [ ] Reports [ ] Notes, observations of pets, plants, science experiments, etc. [ ] Labeling [ ] How to do something [ ] Learning logs [ ] Venn diagram [ ] Write word problems for math [ ] Use of technology [ ] Record experiences or observations [ ] News articles [ ] Time lines [ ] Diagrams [ ] Maps [ ] Surveys [ ] Interviews [ ] Graphs [ ] Brochures [ ] Newsletters [ ] Recipes [ ] Commercials [ ] Calendars [ ] Posters [ ] Information on a report [ ] Writing to learn science, math, social studies, art, foreign language, etc.

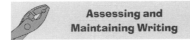

Diagnosis of and Prescriptions for Writing

On the following pages are examples of comments you would find on a Diagnosis of and Prescriptions for Writing chart. The purpose of this chart is to help you interpret student work by comparing student work samples to the written descriptions of various writing problems students may experience. Use the descriptors to diagnose the problems and then assign students to groups (or individual work, if necessary) where prescribed mini-lessons will be taught. These mini-lessons are intended to help move students to the next level of writing skills. Groups should be fluid and created as needed based on continual assessment. Students working together to clear up one problem will not necessarily be in the same group to work on another skill. You may see some students with only a couple of these problems, while some students will have many layers of the problems listed, as well as other problems. For students with many writing challenges, correct the easiest problems first, working on one skill at a time.

The sample problems listed reflect some of the descriptors of development listed on the Writing Profile Chart: Stages of Writing Development (page 26). These are skills targeted for young writers. The blank Diagnosis of and Prescriptions for Writing chart on page 35 will allow you to make comments about student writers. To make keeping track of the paperwork easier, attach each student's charts to the individual work sample you are evaluating, and file the sample and the chart for later reference. If you write notes about more than one student on the Diagnosis of and Prescriptions for Writing chart, cut apart the sections in order to staple them to the work. This way, each student's name and date will be included because the chart is attached to the writing sample.

DIAGNOSIS OF AND PRESCRIPTIONS FOR WRITING

Diagnosis	Student Names/Dates	Prescription
The picture addresses the prompt. Uses random letters. No representation of words. Writes with strings of letters.	Kendra (Sept. 6)	Point out positive things in the paper. Model these with student: • Brainstorming • Phonemic awareness activities • Verbalize sounds Consistently verbalize sounds in daily practice.
The picture addresses the prompt. Some letters used to represent entire words (for example the letter "c" for car).	Shaun (Sept. 6) Rashad (Sept. 6) Millie (Sept. 7)	Point out positive things in the papers. Practice sounding words and stretching to hear sounds beyond the first letter.
The focus is on the topic. Writes using a string of connected letters with no spaces between words.	Hannah (Sept. 6) Cameron (Sept. 8)	Point out positive things in the papers. Demonstrate the difference between a letter and a word. Model writing sentences using periods and exaggerated spacing in sentences on large chart paper so students can see it. Model spacing in daily writing with students.
The focus is not on the topic, but rather on using correct spacing. Ideas are expressed using consonants and words.	Carter (Sept. 6) Denise (Sept. 7) Troy (Sept. 7)	Point out positive things in the papers. Choose two writing samples to share - one that is focused - one that is not. Discuss the differences. (focused paper: sticks to a main topic. All details relate to the topic and are relevant.) Give a new prompt. Brainstorm ideas together before writing.

Assessing and Maintaining Writing **DIAGNOSIS OF AND PRESCRIPTIONS FOR WRITING**

Diagnosis	Student Names/Dates	Prescription
Uses print symbols. Letters are not formed correctly. Random lines cover the paper. Student can tell about own writing.	Michael (Sept. 6) Jamie (Sept. 6) Janette (Sept. 8)	Point out positive things in the papers. Teach correct formation of letters. Give students manuscript alphabet desk tapes to reference for correct formation of letters.
Letters and words are all over the page. Student can tell about own writing.	Mia (Sept. 8)	Point out positive things in the paper. Model tracking print from left to right. Use a pointer to model reading from left to right and top to bottom when engaged in shared reading. Make an "x" on the paper to show student where to begin writing. Use lined paper.
Sentences are focused on the topic, but lack detail.	Lonnie (Sept. 6) Shanita (Sept. 6) Dewayne (Sept. 7) Pam (Sept. 9) Calvin (Sept. 9)	Point out positive things in the papers. Read a variety of books to students as examples of good writing. Write a short paper as a class. Choose a topic. Add details and descriptive words using the five senses and the question words (who, what, when, where, why, how). Add action to create a more descriptive paper. Record the story on chart paper and display it for students to reread as they wish.

DIAGNOSIS OF AND PRESCRIPTIONS FOR WRITING

Diagnosis	Student Names/Dates	Prescription
Sentences are focused on the topic, but are not in logical order (sequence).	Hong (Sept. 6) Terry (Sept. 7) Anna (Sept. 7) Greg (Sept. 8) Delaney (Sept. 8)	Point out positive things in the papers. Create two writing samples to share, one in correct sequence, one not. Discuss the differences. Cut apart the sentences in the second paper, and with student input, paste the sentences in correct order. Read books to students as examples of good writing. Have students write directions for completing a task (for example, how to make a peanut butter and jelly sandwich) to show the importance of sequence.
All sentences begin the same way.	Priscilla (Sept. 6) Ricardo (Sept. 7) Jay (Sept. 9) Virginia (Sept. 9)	Point out positive things in the papers. Let students underline or highlight the beginnings of each sentence. Let students discover that the sentences all begin alike. Brainstorm ways to begin sentences. Rewrite the beginnings of the sentences in the papers, with student input. Point out a variety of sentence beginnings when sharing good literature with students.

DIAGNOSIS OF AND PRESCRIPTIONS FOR WRITING

Diagnosis	Student Names/Dates	Prescription
Ideas are expressed using phonemic spelling but not using standard spelling. The focus is on the topic, using one or two basic ideas.	Mia (Sept. 6) Janette (Sept. 8) Lonnie (Sept. 9)	Point out positive things in the papers. Review phonemic awareness skills. Highlight words in the papers for students to spell using classroom references, by sounding out letters, or with your help.
There is use of temporary spelling, but the paper can be read. The focus is on the topic, but the story is short with only one or two sentences.	Lonnie (Sept. 7) Delaney (Sept. 7) Greg (Sept. 8)	Point out positive things in the papers. Read some well-written papers of an acceptable length. Read a paper that is too short. Let students discuss ways to add details to the story. Review the question words (who, what, where, when, why, how). Record students' ideas as you revise a story on chart paper with them.
There is an absence of punctuation. Sentences are short and repetitive. Uses standard spelling.	Stella (Sept. 6) Calvin (Sept. 6) Linnea (Sept. 9) Mac (Sept. 9)	Point out positive things in the papers. Create sample papers lacking punctuation. Review rules for punctuation (period, question mark, capital letters for proper names and at the beginning of sentences). Allow students to correct the sample papers.

Diagnosis	Student Names/Dates	Prescription

Anecdotal Notes

Anecdotal notes are comments you record as you observe students. They are intended to focus on what students are able to do. Notes are collected over a period of time, assessed for information, and used to determine patterns of development or areas of need for specific instruction. Anecdotal notes allow for quick, informal assessment on a continual basis and should be taken regularly for each student. They should be objective statements and should be dated. Your notes do not need to be formal or extremely detailed, but they should be clear and dated for the sake of documentation and later reference as you assess needs for future instruction. Schedule a few students each day for observation, thereby assuring ongoing assessment for each student without creating an overwhelming task for yourself. Refer to the Writing Profile Chart: Stages for Writing Development (pages 26-27) for a list of abilities a developing writer is working to achieve.

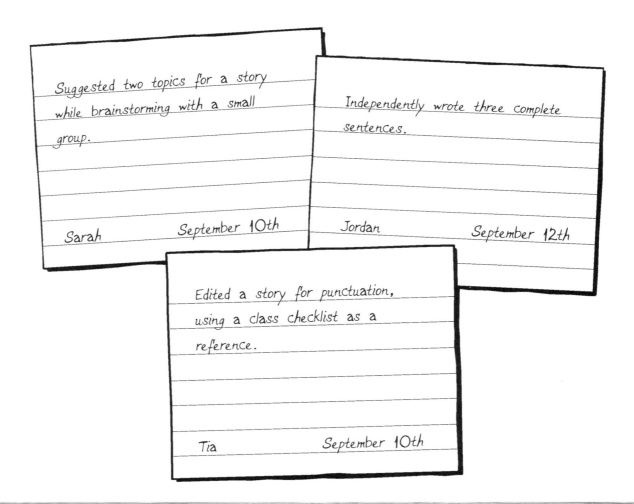

Suggested two topics for a story while brainstorming with a small group.

Sarah   September 10th

Independently wrote three complete sentences.

Jordan   September 12th

Edited a story for punctuation, using a class checklist as a reference.

Tia   September 10th

There are a variety of ways to manage note taking. You may record information on index cards on a clipboard, in a record book, on sticky notes, or in any fashion that works for you. If you choose to use a clipboard and index cards, write each student's name at the bottom of a card. Then, attach the card to the clipboard by taping across the top of the card. Attach the cards beginning at bottom of the clipboard, one slightly on top of the other so that they flip up and are easy to use. When filled, file the cards in each child's writing folder. Five 4" x 6" index cards fit easily on a standard clipboard. You may choose to divide the class into five groups and prepare a clipboard for each group. Assign a day of the week to each group, and you have an instant schedule for assessment.

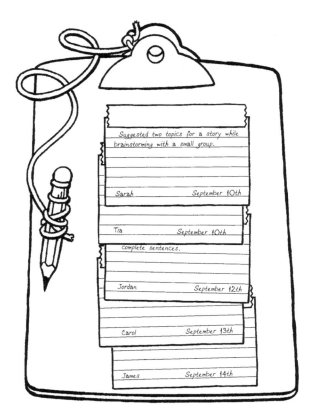

Teacher Checklist for Effective Writing

There are many things to remember as you plan writing instruction. On page 38 is a checklist to consider as you plan. This self-evaluation checklist has been developed for you to use several times during the year to assess whether writing is being promoted and nurtured continually. Take an assessment when school begins and the writing program is started, one near the middle of the school year (possibly January), and one towards the end of the school year (maybe April). This will provide insight into what needs to be improved as the year progresses. As you note the statements for which you check "no," set realistic goals for yourself throughout the year. No one expects you to do everything well at once. The idea is to guide students to become proficient writers, which you will do by becoming an effective writing teacher. Each time you evaluate yourself, choose one or two areas of improvement and decide on a plan of action which is realistic and easy for you to implement.

Yes	No	Assessing and Maintaining Writing **TEACHER CHECKLIST FOR EFFECTIVE WRITING**
		Self-Evaluation
		I encourage a classroom climate where writing is valued and all efforts are respected.
		I create an atmosphere where students feel comfortable sharing opinions and are willing to stretch beyond skills already mastered.
		I provide a print-rich environment where students can reference charts, posters, lists, bulletin boards, and other materials to help them as they write.
		I give students time to talk about their writing.
		I assign writing partners who work together to revise, edit, and share writing.
		I plan lessons based on my state/district goals required for writing proficiency for my grade level, and on my assessment of individual student's needs.
		I maintain high expectations for all students.
		I continually watch and listen to students as they work and maintain assessment records/samples in student portfolios or notebooks.
		I share portfolios/notebooks with parents on a regular basis to keep them informed.
		I plan regular conferences with individual students.
		I set a block of time in the daily schedule for planned writing activities.
		I plan thematic writing activities based on topics being studied across the curriculum to connect writing to reading, math, science, and social studies.
		I find out about students' interests and am accepting of students' choices for writing.
		I write and share my writing with students daily.
		I model the steps in the writing process and demonstrate thinking aloud about my writing.
		I expose all students to a wide variety of text.
		I provide all students an opportunity to write for a variety of audiences.
		I provide all students an opportunity to write in a variety of genres.
		I celebrate writing often for students by encouraging them to publish and share their own work and respectfully listen to the work of others.
		I display student writing for classroom and school recognition, appreciating the writing of students at all developmental levels.

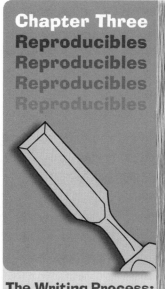
The Writing Process:
Brainstorming and Prewriting

The writing process is composed of specific, related steps that guide the writer from planning what to write to publishing and sharing writing with others. The steps are:

- prewriting—thinking about and planning writing
- drafting—quickly putting thoughts on paper
- revising—reworking the shape and organization of a paper
- editing—reviewing for spelling, grammar, usage, and mechanics
- evaluating—reflecting about what has been written
- publishing—sharing writing with others

At any given time, students will be at various stages in the process and will be writing at their ability levels. For example, Nolan may publish a paragraph and illustration while Juan writes a play to be performed by the class. Design and display a Stages of Writing chart or bulletin board. As you model and teach each step in the process, display writing samples beside the appropriate steps to help students visualize the steps.

It may seem impossible to model and teach all of the steps while providing a variety of activities to encourage writing growth at all levels, but you will find resources in the remainder of this book to help you do just that. By familiarizing yourself with these stages, you will be able to help students become comfortable with them. Give each student a copy of The Writing Process: Stages of Writing reproducible (page 40) to keep at her desk. Encourage students to write notes on their reproducibles on the lines provided to help them remember and understand the stages.

The Writing Process
STAGES OF WRITING

Prewriting

Drafting

Revising

Editing

Evaluating

Publishing

Notes

Brainstorming and Prewriting

Focusing on prewriting introduces students to all of the different ways a writer plans for writing. During this time, students generate ideas and experiment with them. It is also a good time to discuss and identify the audience (who the writing is directed to: classmates, a pen pal, the principal, the president, etc.) and the purpose of the writing (inform, persuade, entertain, describe, etc.).

You can help students generate ideas by sharing with them a wealth of resources that can spark ideas for writing.

- Expose students to a variety of literature by reading aloud daily.
- Read poetry related to a particular topic.
- Share magazines, photos, or pictures from books, then discuss what is occurring in each.
- Engage in storytelling by creating verbal stories to share.
- Brainstorm ideas with the class. Record the ideas on chart paper and store them or post them in the classroom to be used later for reference.
- Bring articles to class related to a particular topic for discussion.
- Using students' ideas, model writing a story for the class.
- Discuss choices for writing related to topics currently being studied in science, reading, math, or social studies.
- Read an excerpt from a story and then watch a film or television clip of the same story excerpt. Discuss and write about how they are alike and different.
- Have students write word problems to demonstrate assigned equations.

Sharing these opportunities with children will give them background experience and will prepare them to participate in prewriting activities like:

- verbalizing before writing
- talking aloud, drawing pictures
- labeling
- listing
- webbing
- using drawing and writing templates
- brainstorming
- gathering information
- observing
- listening
- reading
- note-taking
- discussing
- charting
- role-playing

Prompts

Sometimes you will ask students to respond to a specific topic or prompt you have chosen (or they may need to practice responding to prompts on standardized tests). You may choose to assess student writing during the year based on responses to a prompt as part of your overall assessment. Any of the following prompts can be used to assess student writing levels.

- You become invisible for one day. Describe what happens to you that day.
- Imagine you are a tour guide for a new student at your school. Write about what you would show to the student, and what you would tell him or her about your school.
- Imagine that you are an ant at a picnic. Write a story about what happens to you.
- Pretend that you can become any animal you choose for one day. Write about what happens when you become that animal.
- Imagine that you meet a robot on the way to school. Write a story about what happens.
- You are granted one wish. Tell about what happens when your wish is granted.
- You are a newspaper reporter who is interviewing a famous person. Write a question-and-answer article that shows what happened during your interview.
- You are applying for a job. Write a business letter explaining to the employer why you would be the best person for the job.
- A cooking magazine wants to publish your favorite recipe. Write the recipe including ingredients, measurements, mixing, cooking, and serving instructions.
- Think about your favorite place to spend a summer day. Write a detailed description about the place.

Once students have chosen topics for writing, they need to prepare to write. There are many techniques to help students prepare to write. An important step in the preparation is verbalizing before writing. Encourage students to talk to each other. This allows students who have not developed a great deal of language experience to listen and get ideas from other students. Students will have the opportunity to brainstorm thoughts and ideas, generate additional topics, visually organize thoughts, choose types of writing, and make plans. Distribute copies of the Ways to Prepare for Writing list on page 43 to help students prepare for writing.

Here are some ways to prepare for writing:

1 Think about the topic.

2 Talk with a writing partner.

3 List words and ideas, and draw pictures for the writing.

4 Choose a purpose for writing.

5 Decide who will be the audience for your writing.

6 Gather information.

7 Organize your ideas.

8 Create a plan for your text.

Planning for Writing

The following forms will help students actively plan for writing. Before asking students to complete these forms, remember the importance of modeling the procedure for completing them. Ask students to work in small groups, in pairs, or independently. Consider using the chalkboard, pieces of chart paper, or the overhead projector to be sure all students can see your writing.

Choosing Your Story

Students often don't have a good grasp of what makes an interesting story. Demonstrate this technique for students. List three story ideas, then discuss them with the class. Next, choose the story that would be the most interesting to write about. Have students work in pairs to complete a Prewriting: Choosing Your Story form (page 45).

Senses Planning Circle

Read a teacher-selected writing prompt to the students. Write the prompt in the middle of a circle (use chart paper or the chalkboard). Around the outside of the circle, write each of the five senses and also the word *emotion*. These will encourage students to think of details about the prompt. Record responses inside the circle near the specific word being discussed. Each word or phrase may represent a sentence or group of sentences in the writing. You may want to number the groups of words in the order in which they will be written. After modeling the process for students, distribute copies of the Senses Planning Circle (page 46) to students and have them repeat the exercise.

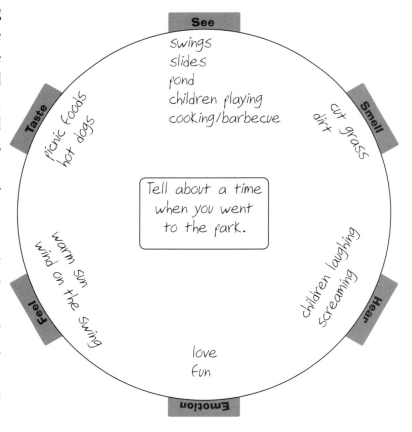

See
swings
slides
pond
children playing
cooking/barbecue

Smell
cut grass
dirt

Taste
picnic foods
hot dogs

Tell about a time when you went to the park.

Hear
children laughing
screaming

Feel
warm sun
wind on the swing

Emotion
love
fun

Name _____ Date _____

You have many stories to tell. This will help you choose a good one.

Write

List three ideas that you think would make a good story.

1. _____

2. _____

3. _____

Discuss

Talk about your story ideas with your writing partner. Tell your partner about the beginning, middle, and end of each story. Which one of the stories do you and your writing partner think will be the best one to tell and write about?

Choose

Write your story idea: _____

_____

This will be the topic of your story.

Place this list of ideas in your writing notebook.

© Carson-Dellosa

The Writing Process:
Brainstorming and Prewriting

SENSES PLANNING CIRCLE

Use the Senses Planning Circle to help you think about what to write.

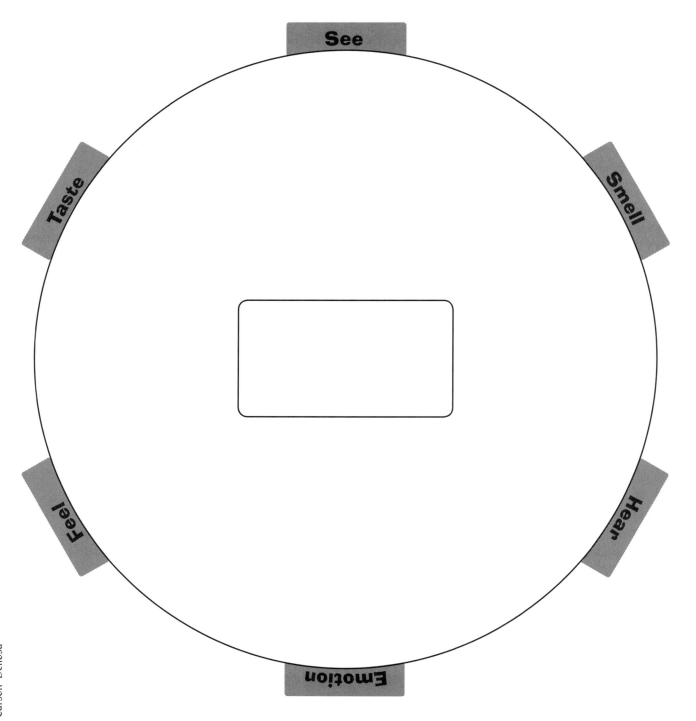

Senses Writing Square

Using the Senses Planning Circle and the Senses Writing Square helps students give more details in their stories. The Senses Planning Circle is a good vehicle to use for planning, and the Senses Writing Square helps organize the first draft. The next step is to write the story on paper. Choose ideas from those listed on the Senses Planning Circle to complete a structured sentence in each box in the Senses Writing Square. Illustrate each sentence.

The Writing Process:
Brainstorming and Prewriting

SENSES WRITING SQUARE

Title: _The Park_

First Sentence(s): _The park is fun. I like to go to the park._

I see _children playing._

I hear _children laughing._

I smell _the hot dogs cooking._

I feel _hungry for lunch._

Conclusion: _I hope to go back to the park tomorrow. It is a fun place to visit._

Name _____ Date _____

SENSES WRITING SQUARE

Title: _____

First Sentence(s): _____

I see _____
_____

I hear _____
_____

I smell _____
_____

I feel _____
_____

Conclusion: _____
_____

Question Word Planning Circle

In addition to the five senses, you may also use the question words (who, what, where, when, why, how), to guide students to visualize the organization of their writing. Record a writing prompt in the center of a Question Word Planning Circle (page 50). Have students write words, phrases, short sentences, or questions on copies of the Question Word Planning Circle to record their ideas for writing.

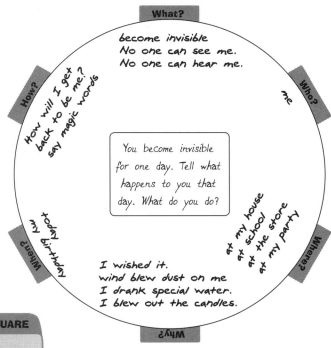

What?
become invisible
No one can see me.
No one can hear me.

How?
How will I get back to be me?
say magic words

Who?
me

You become invisible for one day. Tell what happens to you that day. What do you do?

Where?
at my house
at school
at the store
at my party

When?
today
my birthday

Why?
I wished it.
wind blew dust on me
I drank special water.
I blew out the candles.

QUESTION WORD WRITING SQUARE

Title: My Invisible Day
First Sentence(s): I became invisible at my birthday party!

First, I blew out the candles on my cake.

Next, I disappeared so no one could see me.

I also could not talk to anyone.

Finally, I wished to be seen again.

Conclusion: I became myself again. I was happy to be back at my birthday party.

Question Word Writing Square

Give students copies of the Question Word Writing Square (page 51) to guide the organization of their writing. Have them choose ideas from their completed Question Word Planning Circles to fill in the blanks and draw pictures.

The Writing Process:
Brainstorming and Prewriting

QUESTION WORD PLANNING CIRCLE

Use the Question Word Planning Circle to help you think about what to write.

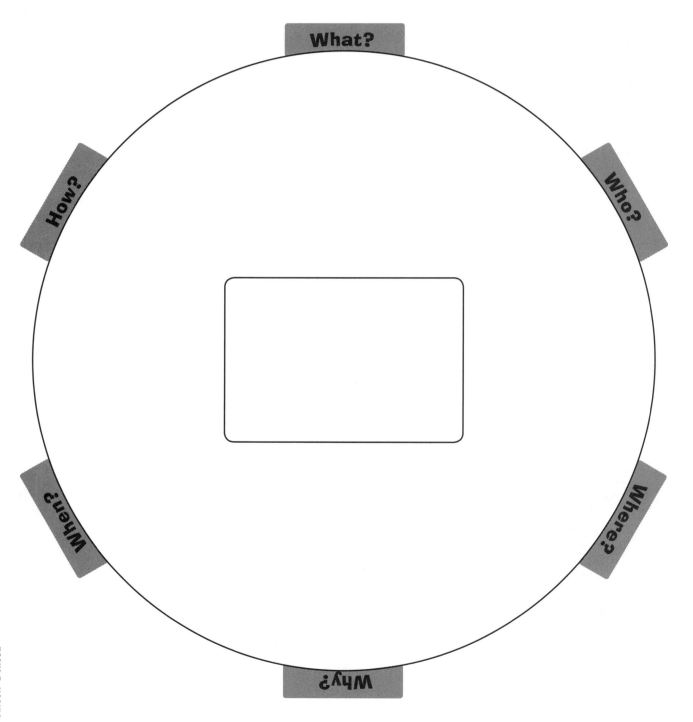

Name _____ Date _____

Title: _____

First Sentence(s): _____

First, I _____

_____

Next, I _____

_____

I also _____

_____

Finally, I _____

_____

Conclusion: _____

_____

Prewriting Story Web

A story web can take any shape you like, and for this reason, it is one of the most popular brainstorming activities. Students love the idea of a web of words. First, draw a small circle in the center of a piece of chart paper. Write the topic in the circle. In smaller circles attached to the main circle, list points to discuss. Think of each small circle as a subtopic for a paragraph, focusing on one characteristic of the main topic. In each small circle, list words or phrases to include in the writing. You may want to number the circles in the order in which the paragraphs will be written.

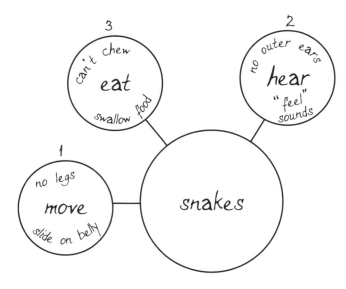

Beginning, Middle, and End Drawing Template/Beginning, Middle, and End Writing Template

As students choose topics and begin to think about their writing, they must consider the flow of information. How does the story begin? What happens in the middle? How will the piece end? There are several ways to help students of all ability levels visualize the organization of their writing. Drawing works better for some students, while writing is more helpful for others. The Beginning, Middle, and End Drawing Template and Beginning, Middle, and End Writing Template use the same template (page 54), but they can be adapted for those who prefer to draw, and others who prefer to write. Students should only focus on organizing thoughts at this time, not correct grammar, punctuation, spelling, etc. That comes later, during the editing stage.

To use the Beginning, Middle, and End Drawing Template, provide copies of it for students, or have each student fold a piece of construction paper into three sections. Then, instruct students to draw pictures to tell what will happen in the beginning, middle, and end of the story. You may want to pair students so that they can discuss their plans and perhaps refine their ideas as they reflect on the input of their peers. See the example on page 53 for what a template may look like when it is complete.

The Beginning, Middle, and End Writing Template (page 54) is a good way for students to plan how the events in the story will flow. Depending on the complexity of each piece, students may write complete sentences as they will appear in the actual story, or they may write short sentences and/or phrases to get ideas on paper. Provide copies of the template for students, or have each student fold a piece of construction paper into three sections. Explain that they should write the beginning of a story in the top area of the map, write the action and details in the middle, and write the end of a story in the bottom section.

The Writing Process:
Brainstorming and Prewriting

BEGINNING, MIDDLE, AND END *Writing Template*

Beginning

I went to the amuzment park
with my family.

Middle

I rode the roller coaster

It was fast and skarey.

My bruther rode the Feruswhel He got stuk
on top!

We ate hot dogs, popcorn, cotun candy, and
ice-cream.

I felt sick for a little whil

End

It was a grate day!

Name _____ Date _____

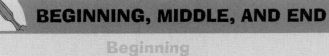

BEGINNING, MIDDLE, AND END

Beginning
Beginning
Beginning

Middle
Middle
Middle

End
End
End

Writing Planning Form

The Writing Planning Form (page 56) is a more structured way to consider the contents of a piece of writing. It includes title, setting, and characters along with action and details. It also requires the writer to consider why the main character takes certain actions. This form is helpful for more advanced writers who attempt sophisticated pieces of writing, but it also gives beginning writers a chance to think about motivation.

Simple Story Map

With the Simple Story Map (page 57) students have freedom to create a prewriting plan. This form also suggests that they focus on setting, which is helpful in preparing students to be more descriptive in their writing. In each box, have students draw and/or write words and phrases to get ideas on paper before writing.

KWL Chart

The KWL Chart (page 58) helps students organize factual information before writing. Students may be writing in response to learning in reading, math, science, or social studies. The chart could be started at the beginning of a unit of study and completed as students plan to write about what they have learned. Students write words, phrases, or short sentences in the first column to record what they already *know* about a topic. In the center, they list questions about what they *want* to learn during the study of the topic. Finally, after study, students write what they have *learned* about the topic. Students can refer to the chart for information to include in their writing.

The Writing Process: Brainstorming and Prewriting

KWL CHART

Topic: **Bears**

Know K	Want to Learn W	Learned L
Bears can be black, brown, or white. Bears can be big or little. Bears sleep in winter.	Why do bears sleep in winter? What do bears eat?	Bears hibernate because they would not be able to find enough food. Bears eat nuts and berries. Some bears eat fish.

Name _____ Date _____

Title of my story: _____

Where it happens: _____

Who it happens to: _____

Beginning
Beginning
Beginning
In the beginning of the story, what is the main character doing?

_____

_____

_____

because _____

Middle
Middle
Middle
In the middle of the story, what is the main character doing?

_____

_____

_____

because _____

End
End
End
At the end of the story, what is the main character doing?

_____

_____

_____

because _____

Name _____ Date _____

Character(s)	Setting

Problem	Solution

Name _____   Date _____

Topic: _____

Know K	Want to Learn W	Learned L

Prewriting Wrap-Up

Prewriting is a very important part of the writing process. It is where the planning and decisions about content and order of writing take place. Introduce as many ideas as possible to help students with their prewriting. Let students have ample time to practice using them. Give students enough time in the prewriting stage, and the other stages of writing will flow much more smoothly.

Prewriting Checklist

After focusing on prewriting, use the Prewriting Checklist (page 60) to assess student progress in this area. After assessment, put the checklists in students' writing folders or portfolios for documentation and as reference for parent conferences.

The Writing Process: Brainstorming and Prewriting		PREWRITING CHECKLIST
Author's Name	**Date**	**Comments**
Mario	10/25	Good prewriting work here!

1. The student can identify the audience for which the piece will be written.

   Mario is able to choose an audience and target his writing to it.

2. The student can identify the purpose for the writing.

   Mario's last paper had a very specific purpose (a friendly letter).

3. The student generates ideas of his/her own from experience.

   Yes, he chose topics from several things he did this summer.

4. The student experiments with a variety of prewriting activities.

   Yes, see attached story webs and Writing Planning Forms.

5. The student shows progress from a previous prewriting piece.

   He is definitely more focused. He generated more ideas this time.

Author's Name	Date	Comments

1. The student can identify the audience for which the piece will be written.

2. The student can identify the purpose for the writing.

3. The student generates ideas of his/her own from experience.

4. The student experiments with a variety of prewriting activities.

5. The student shows progress from a previous prewriting piece.

The Writing Process: Drafting

The purpose of drafting is simply to put ideas on paper. Sometimes a writing draft is called a "sloppy copy" because the emphasis is placed on putting thoughts, feelings, and ideas into concrete form without concern for neat handwriting or correct spelling, punctuation, or grammar. Those items will be addressed in the editing stage. At this point, students question, "Where should I begin?" They record their ideas in rough form. They try story ideas to see where they lead. Students write and share ideas with partners, small groups, or the entire class. You conference with students to check on the progress of writing drafts. Students also conference with peers to get validation for writing completed thus far, as well as suggestions for improvement. Students should feel free to change their ideas and start again if necessary.

In order to put thoughts on paper, students must know the words they need to express themselves. The greater the vocabulary, the better the expression. The following information and activities will help students expand their vocabulary and practice putting thoughts on paper when drafting.

100 High-Frequency Words

Certain words make up the majority of text found in any piece of writing. They are called high-frequency words due to the frequency with which they appear. Students need to practice using these words until spelling them becomes second nature. Students will not become fluent writers until they internalize a basic vocabulary they can use to express

themselves. Begin exposing students to these words by choosing a few to display on word cards on a wall in the classroom. Each day, review some of the words with students. Each week, add more words to the wall.

There are many activities you can organize using the high-frequency words on the wall. Depending on ability level, choose students to find words that start with a selected beginning or ending consonant sound, start with a specific vowel sound, have two syllables, are nouns, etc. It's a great way to use that minute or two spent waiting while students are transitioning from one activity to another. The wall also becomes a source for students to reference when writing. They should learn to check the wall to find the correct spelling of many words they use regularly.

100 High-Frequency Words

a	find	like	said	was
about	first	long	see	way
all	for	look	she	we
an	from		so	were
and		make	some	what
are	get	many		when
as	give	may	than	where
at	go	more	that	which
		my	the	who
be	had		their	will
been	has	no	them	with
but	have	not	then	word
by	he	now	there	would
	her	number	these	
call	him		they	your
can	his	of	this	you're
come	how	off	those	
could		on	time	
	I	one	to	
day	if	or	too	
did	in	other	two	
do	is	out		
down	it		up	
	its	part	use	
each	it's			

Thematic Word Posters

Students need good resources to reference when they are trying to choose the right words for writing. Thematic word posters give students a variety of words to reference, and they may help students take their writing in different directions. For example, write the word *orange* in the center of a piece of chart paper. Have students look in the environment for things that are orange and try to name other things they know are orange. Record the related words on the chart around the word in the center of the page. When the chart is complete, laminate the page and display the chart where it can easily be seen by all students.

Thematic Word Poster: Orange

Thematic Word Poster: Said

Thematic word posters are also good for displaying better choices for overused words such as said. Students can suggest alternatives or use a thesaurus to come up with a list of more interesting and precise word choices. Challenge students to come up with very unusual words.

To go along with the thematic word posters about colors, students can create and illustrate individual books about colors (for example) during independent work at a writing center or art center. Encourage students to make thematic books and word posters according to different curriculum areas, such as animals or weather for science, a local landmark or recent field trip for social studies, etc.

Sentence Builder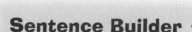

You must model for students the process for building an interesting descriptive sentence. Before working with students, enlarge the Sentence Builder (page 66) or use a piece of chart paper folded lengthwise. If possible, laminate the chart paper or reproducible for continued use. (If laminated, use an erasable marker.) At the top of the paper write a simple sentence such as, "The dog barked." On the left side of the paper write directions to suggest what can be added to make a better sentence.

- Add when.
- Add size or color.
- Name a place.
- Add a name.

The simple sentence written at the top of the paper will be rewritten on the right side of the paper as you add suggested details from students.

- Yesterday, the dog barked.
- Yesterday, the brown dog barked.
- Yesterday, the brown dog barked in the doghouse.
- Yesterday, Joey's brown dog barked in the doghouse.

The last sentence is a more descriptive choice for student writing. Display the chart for students to reference. Make this type of activity a daily group activity for a week so that students can practice building sentences.

The Writing Process: Drafting   **SENTENCE BUILDER**

Simple Sentence: *The dog barked.*

Directions	More Descriptive Sentence
Add when.	*Yesterday, the dog barked.*
Add size or color.	*Yesterday, the brown dog barked.*
Name a place.	*Yesterday, the brown dog barked in the doghouse.*
Add a name.	*Yesterday, Joey's brown dog barked in the doghouse.*

The Writing Process:
Drafting

SENTENCE BUILDER

Simple Sentence: _____

Directions	More Descriptive Sentence
Add when.	_____ _____ _____ _____
Add size or color.	_____ _____ _____ _____
Name a place.	_____ _____ _____ _____
Add a name.	_____ _____ _____

Sentence Structure Chart

Before making this chart with students, review what must be included to make a sentence. Most sentences include a subject, a verb, an object, and some type of punctuation. Before working with students, write several simple sentences on chart paper, using a different colored marker to represent each part of the sentence. Write the subject of the sentence in red marker, write the verb with a green marker, write the object with a black marker, and record the punctuation with a blue marker. Before naming the parts of a sentence for the students, let them decide why the words are written in different colors. Guide them to discover the parts of a sentence. After they notice the pattern between colors and words, they are ready to use the Sentence Structure Chart (page 69). This activity is good for reviewing information from reading, science, math, and social studies while strengthening writing skills.

For example, write "Pumpkins have _____." on an enlarged copy of the Sentence Structure Chart or on chart paper. Have students read the sentence as you write it, then brainstorm a list of words that would complete the sentence sensibly. Use a black marker, representing the object of the sentence, to record their responses under the word *have* on the chart. (Student responses are depicted in the illustration on page 68 as broken lines). Repeat the process for "Pumpkins are _____." Remind students that sentences can be made by choosing one word and punctuation mark of each color. Have them create and write a variety of sentences by choosing words and punctuation marks from the chart, such as:

- Pumpkins have lines.
- Pumpkins have seeds.
- Pumpkins have stems.
- Pumpkins have pulp.
- Pumpkins are orange.
- Pumpkins are big.
- Pumpkins are heavy.
- Pumpkins are food.

For students who need extra help, provide sheets of paper prepared with colored lines so students can match the line color with a word or punctuation mark of the same color.

_____   _____   _____   _____

    (red)   (green)   (black)   (blue)

SENTENCE STRUCTURE CHART

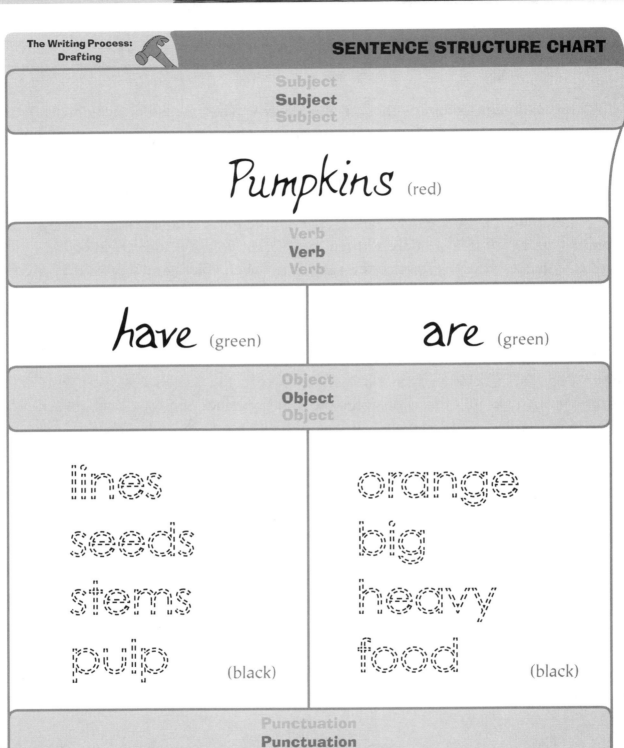

Subject

Pumpkins (red)

Verb

have (green)   *are* (green)

Object

lines   orange
seeds   big
stems   heavy
pulp   (black)   food   (black)

Punctuation

 (blue)   (blue)

The Writing Process: Drafting

SENTENCE STRUCTURE CHART

Subject
Subject
Subject

Verb
Verb
Verb

Object
Object
Object

Punctuation
Punctuation
Punctuation

The Writing Process: Revision

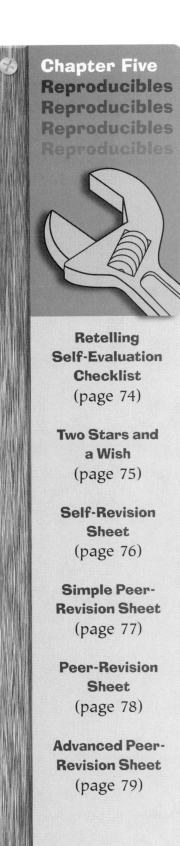

During revision, students are looking at writing to check if the ideas are clear and the purpose is evident to the reader. It is a time to share with a writing buddy in order to improve the content, organization, and coherence of a piece. The revision stage of the writing process includes many of the same activities as prewriting. Students continue to explore ideas and replan and rewrite to improve their piece of writing. It is not a time to recopy the "sloppy copy" on good paper.

Revising a piece of writing can be overwhelming. It is easier to model small revision steps with students before moving to more complex ideas. Mini-lessons are the perfect format for teaching revision strategies. For example, model during a mini-lesson how to add descriptive words or more exciting verbs, or how to delete unnecessary words. Let students practice changing words before moving to a mini-lesson about sentences. In the mini-lesson, explain that sentences can be combined. Encourage students to try a variety of beginnings and to try varying the lengths of sentences. Model each activity and let students experiment with their writing.

Next, move to adding information. Students can share their writing with peers or small groups, and ask for input. Students may ask the writer to include more information to answer questions they have about the writing. The most difficult revision technique to teach is when to remove information. Model how to review an initial piece of writing and take out sentences that do not relate to the topic or are weak and contain unnecessary words. Give students opportunities to practice looking over their own writing to remove irrelevant information.

Then, move to paragraph revision. Students must learn to check for a logical sequence of information, moving sentences when appropriate. They will begin to use transition words (first, next, then, finally, etc.) to move from one paragraph to the next. During the revision stage, students also will learn to vary the length of the paragraphs.

Students also need to learn how to write effective beginnings and endings. Expose students to effective ways to create a variety of beginnings and endings by sharing different types of picture books and other literature with them. Point out the method each author uses to get their attention at the beginning or bring closure to the end. Let students hear several stories and then vote for the one with the best beginning or ending. How did the author make them want to hear more? Then, have the class discuss the choices and list the characteristics that made one piece of writing better than another. Students do not have to agree on the best piece of writing. The goal is to get each student to take an objective look at the beginning or ending of a piece of writing, come to a decision about why it is good, and transfer those characteristics to his own writing.

There are a few additional topics students need to understand before they can become proficient in revision. Many topics can be addressed in specific mini-lessons at the beginning of a Writer's Workshop session. Remember to address only one issue during a mini-lesson. Here are a few examples.

- staying on topic
- adding relevant supporting details
- deleting unnecessary words and irrelevant details
- using descriptive words
- using words to create a picture in the mind of the reader
- looking for logical order or sequence of events
- expanding vocabulary to make better word choices
- working with a partner, small group, or whole group to provide and accept thoughtful feedback as an author

There are several techniques you can use to address the revision process with students. Begin by modeling instruction and conferencing with students regarding their progress. Allow students to conference with peers in pairs or small groups, or to participate in self-conferences by using the Retelling Self-Evaluation Checklist (page 74) or the Self-Revision Sheet (page 76).

Retelling Self-Evaluation Checklist

Students learn a great deal about writing and gain a "sense of story" from retelling stories you read to them. Each week, introduce students to retelling by sharing a familiar story, such as a fairy tale. Fairy tales are usually familiar to most students and are easy to retell. Read the story to students one day. The next day, tell students you want to share the story with them again, without using the book. Give each student a copy of the Retelling Self-Evaluation Checklist (page 74). You may want to use an overhead projector to model this lesson. Tell students that you want to include important parts of the story when you retell with them, so this list will be your guide for what to share. Go over each item on the list and ask students to listen as you retell the story to see if you cover everything. Leave the transparency on the overhead for students to refer to while you retell the story. Afterward, go back over the list and have students determine if all items were addressed.

When you have shared and retold several stories, have students pick one to retell to a partner. After retelling, have each student fill out an evaluation checklist either by herself or with input from her partner. Students may write and also illustrate the retelling. You may want to bind these stories into books and place them in a reading center for students to reread during the year. Eventually, have students move to retelling experiences they have had in the same way as they retell stories they have read.

Two Stars and a Wish

As the author shares a piece of writing the first time, students should listen in order to understand the message. During the second reading, students should listen critically and be prepared to offer two positive comments (two stars) and one "wish" that would improve the paper. A "wish" is often a request for an addition to the story to clear up confusion. For example, after hearing a piece written about a student getting a new bike, students may say:

- "I'm glad you wrote about your new bike. We all like to hear about birthday presents."
- "You used words that really helped me see how your bike looks."
- "I wish you would tell about some of the places you have ridden it."

Model this technique with students before asking them to use it. Help students understand that all comments can be positive, even when asking for more information or clarification. Use the Two Stars and a Wish form (page 75) for this exercise.

Students will be reviewing their own writing, and will often be working in pairs or in small groups to share writing and provide feedback to each other. You may want to make a chart from the following sentences to remind students to seek input.

- Have a peer read your story.
- Listen for areas that need attention.
- Read your writing to a small group and ask for helpful comments.
- Make changes to improve your piece of writing.

Self and Peer Revision

Students can use one of the following checklists to gather input to improve writing. There are several levels represented in the revision worksheets in order to help both beginning and more advanced writers learn how to revise their writing.

Self-Revision Sheet (page 76)

The first worksheet has three programmed sections and five for you to program. The student takes a good look at her writing and chooses certain areas on which to focus in order to improve her work. Other possible areas to use include spelling, grammar, punctuation, characterization, description and detail, and fluency.

Simple Peer-Revision Sheet (page 77)

This worksheet helps beginning writers who need to answer broad questions about their writing. Even students capable of writing only a few sentences can handle these questions. It also includes six programmable spaces.

Peer-Revision Sheet (page 78)

The Peer-Revision Sheet is more complicated than the Simple Peer-Revision Sheet in that a student gets several opinions on his writing. You can leave this sheet open-ended, or before students review, you can ask them to focus on a specific area of text. You may even have different reviewers focus on different areas. Students can grow into this sheet with some instruction.

Advanced Peer-Revision Sheet (page 79)

Of the three revision sheets, this is the most specific. It includes three programmable spaces. One student completes this entire sheet while reviewing one paper. You may want to alter some of the questions, if, for example, students read silently to themselves or you want to focus on different areas.

Name _____ Date _____

RETELLING SELF-EVALUATION CHECKLIST

Self-Evaluation
Self-Evaluation
Self-Evaluation

Yes	No	Check a box under yes or no to show whether or not you agree with each statement.
		I named the title and author.
		I began with the introduction.
		I told where and when the story took place.
		I told the story in order.
		I remembered all of the important events.
		I told about all of the important characters.
		I told some important details.
		I told how the story ended.
		I used an expressive voice.

My goals to improve my retelling skills are:

1. _____

_____

2. _____

_____

3. _____

_____

On a separate sheet of paper, write the retelling of the story. Make sure to write in complete sentences and practice good presentation skills.

My Name _____ Date _____

Author's Name _____

Title of Story _____

Two Stars

I liked:

1. _____

_____

_____

2. _____

_____

_____

A Wish

I wish:

1. _____

_____

_____

Name _____ Date _____

Yes	No	Self-Evaluation
		Check a box under yes or no to show whether or not you agree with each statement.
		My writing makes sense when I read it.
		I chose words that help to make a picture for the reader.
		My story has a beginning, a middle, and an end.

My Name _____ Date _____

Author's Name _____

Title of Story _____

		The Writing Process: Revision

SIMPLE PEER-REVISION SHEET

Peer Evaluation
Peer Evaluation
Peer Evaluation

Yes	No	Check a box under yes or no to show whether or not you agree with each statement.
		The story stays on topic.
		The story makes sense.

© Carson-Dellosa

Name _____   Date _____

Title of Story _____

    PEER-REVISION SHEET

This is a story I have chosen to share. Please write a thoughtful comment to help me improve my writing.

Comments	Signatures

My Name _____ Date _____

Author's Name _____

Title of Story _____

The Writing Process: Revision		ADVANCED PEER-REVISION SHEET
Yes	**No**	**Peer Evaluation** Check a box under yes or no to answer each question.
		Did my partner read the story to me, and did I follow along?
		Does the story make sense throughout?
		Does the writer have good ideas?
		Does the story have a beginning, a middle, and an end?
		Is this an interesting piece of writing?

Comments: _____

_____

_____

_____

_____

_____

_____

The Writing Process: Editing

Self-Editing Checklist
(page 82)

Peer-Editing Checklist
(page 83)

Peer-Editing Record
(page 84)

The Editing Hand
(page 85)

Students have put thoughts on paper. They have considered the topic, the purpose, and audience for whom they are writing. They have reviewed the logical organization of their writing. They have sought input from you and from their peers to improve their writing. Now, the goal is to correct errors in spelling, grammar, usage, and mechanics.

During the editing stage, students identify and correct errors by applying previously learned rules. They may reference materials in the classroom to help determine how to make needed corrections. They can check their own progress or conference with you, peers, or small groups. They may determine specific items to look for in their writing by referencing an editing checklist chart that is displayed in the classroom.

With students, generate a checklist of things to edit on their papers. The checklist may contain only a few items at the beginning of the year but will grow as students develop more skills. A basic editing checklist includes the following:
- Did the writer start sentences with capital letters?
- Are names of people and places capitalized?
- Did the writer correctly use punctuation at the end of each sentence?
- Did the writer spell most of the words correctly?
- Is the handwriting neat and easy to read?

Many editing skills can be taught as mini-lessons during Writer's Workshop. Prepare mini-lessons that focus on the following conventions of print.

- spelling rules and patterns
- sentence fluency
- subject/verb agreement
- how to use simple proofreader's marks

- capitalization
- punctuation
- how to use an editor's checklist

Several checklists and forms are provided. Choose those that suit each student's abilities.

Self-Editing Checklist

A student may edit a piece of his own writing by checking himself against the criteria on the Self-Editing Checklist (page 82). The student can make necessary corrections before conferencing with you or peers.

Peer-Editing Checklist

The Peer-Editing Checklist (page 83) can be used by writing partners, small groups, or the whole class. Before students begin to edit peer writing, review some editing basics, such as using positive language, marking things clearly, etc.

Peer-Editing Record

The Peer-Editing Record (page 84) is an open-ended form appropriate for use by more advanced writers. You may want to model writing a sample of this form with small groups or the whole class. Having space to write without specific directions can be overwhelming, so teach students how to focus on one or two important issues, unless they are marking all aspects of grammar, spelling, capitalization, and punctuation. Even then, students may only need to comment on one or two areas.

The Editing Hand

Enlarge a copy of the Editing Hand (page 85) to display for classroom reference. Students may want to keep smaller, individual copies in their writing portfolios or folders. Model for students how to use the simple proofreader's marks shown on the palm of the hand. Give students many opportunities to practice. Use the examples below to begin.

⬭	Check spelling	(The dog ⬭kame⬭ home.)
≡	Capital letter needed	(h̲e ran to the store.)
∧	Add something	(William wanted ∧cat.) a

Name _____   Date _____

SELF-EDITING CHECKLIST

Self-Evaluation

Yes	No	Check a box under yes or no to show whether or not you agree with each statement.
		I used capital letters.
		I used periods.
		I checked the spelling of some words.
		I used my best handwriting.
		I drew pictures that go with my writing.
		I can improve my writing by _____.

My Name _____ Date _____

Author's Name _____

Title of Story _____

PEER-EDITING CHECKLIST

Peer Evaluation
Peer Evaluation
Peer Evaluation

Yes	No	
		Check a box under yes or no to answer each question.
		Does the writing have:
		correct letter formation?
		correct spacing?
		capital letters for words that begin sentences?
		capital letters for names?
		capital letters for days and months?
		correct punctuation at the ends of sentences?
		most words spelled correctly?
		How can the author improve the writing?

© Carson-Dellosa

Author's Name _____

The Writing Process: Editing	PEER-EDITING RECORD		
Date	**Peer Editor**	**Title or Topic**	**Comments**

Author's self-assessment: _____

_____

_____

_____

_____

The Editing Hand

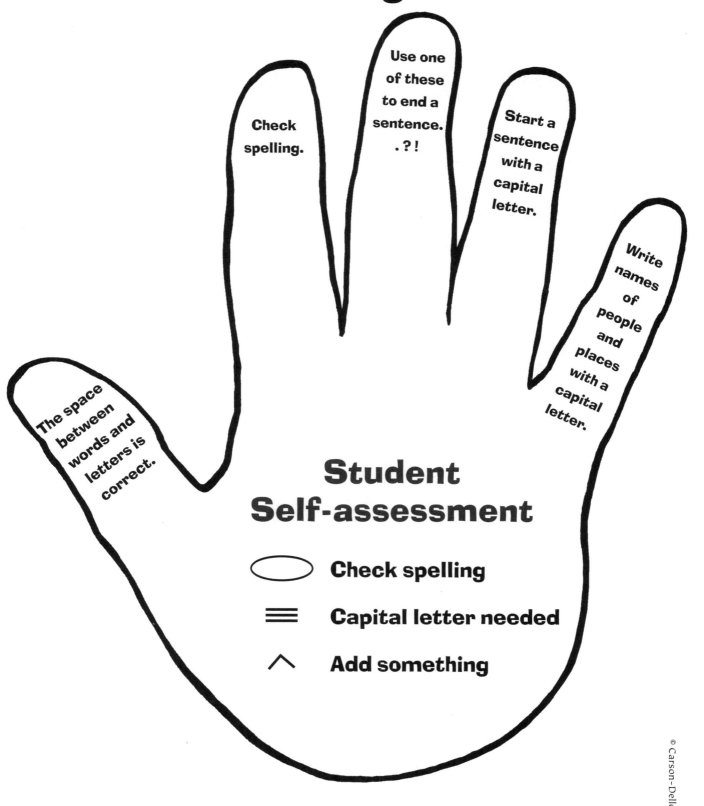

Check spelling.

Use one of these to end a sentence. . ? !

Start a sentence with a capital letter.

Write names of people and places with a capital letter.

The space between words and letters is correct.

Student Self-assessment

◯   **Check spelling**

≡   **Capital letter needed**

∧   **Add something**

The Writing Process:
Evaluating and Publishing

Chapter Seven
Reproducibles
Reproducibles
Reproducibles
Reproducibles

Writing Reflection Sheet #1
(page 87)

Writing Reflection Sheet #2
(page 88)

Flip Book
(page 90)

Evaluating

The process of evaluation helps students think about what they have learned from their writing experiences. Evaluating writing empowers students by providing opportunities for self-assessment, reflection, and goal setting. Students may share as a group how to make writing better, or they may use prepared reflection sheets to consider their writing experiences. As a class, create a list of ways to improve writing. Display it for students to reference during their next writing experiences. Some ideas to include are:

- create an exciting beginning
- add more details
- make a character talk
- choose descriptive words
- choose more interesting action words

Sometimes it is easier for a student to reflect on a writing experience if he is given a form to use as a guide. See pages 87 and 88 for two examples of simple reflection sheets. Writing Reflection Sheet #1 helps students think about positive aspects of writing and possible improvements, while Writing Reflection Sheet #2 helps students focus on the experience as well. Students may choose to share their reflections with the group or keep them in writing folders or portfolios. They will find it useful to review their reflection sheets during the year to note writing growth.

The Writing Process:
Evaluating and Publishing

WRITING REFLECTION SHEET #1

I am good at
I am good at
I am good at

I need to work on
I need to work on
I need to work on

Name _____ Date _____

What did you enjoy most?

_____

_____

_____

_____

_____

What was the hardest part of the writing process for you?

_____

_____

_____

_____

What are some other things you would like to write about?

_____

_____

_____

_____

Publishing

Students have written, revised, polished, and evaluated their ideas. During the publishing stage of writing, they communicate those ideas to an audience. There are many ways to publish. Students can:

- create a book and design a cover
- make a big book, flip book, or shape book
- attach the writing to the center of a poster and use the surrounding area for illustrations
- turn the writing into a play or a puppet show
- display writing on the walls of the classroom and in the hallway
- share writing orally within the class
- share writing orally with another class
- tape record the story to go into a reading/listening center
- combine class writings on a particular topic into a class book

There are several publishing mini-lesson ideas that you can model for students, such as how to:

- make writing look its best for presentation
- present to an audience
- be part of an audience
- create different kinds of books

There are many different kinds of books students can make. Following are directions for three. As a strategy for separating publishing from other writing, make sure that this writing has been though the stages in the writing process.

Flip Book

To make a flip book, place two sheets of paper (8½" x 11") with the back sheet 1½" higher than the front sheet. Bring the bottom of both sheets up toward the opposite edges of the papers. Align the edges so that all are the same distance apart, then fold. Staple the pages together along the fold. Have students write the titles of their stories on the top sheets. They can organize their stories on the layered pages using one page for the beginning, one for the middle, and one for the end of the story. Illustrations to accompany the story can be drawn on each flipped-up page. See page 90 for an example.

Flip Book

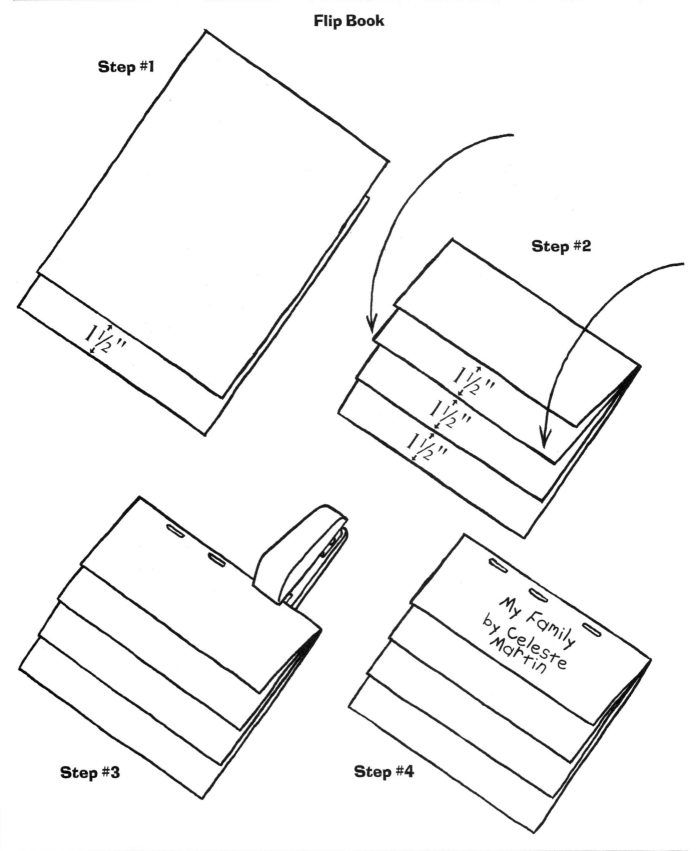

Step #1

1½"

Step #2

1½"
1½"
1½"

Step #3

Step #4

My Family
by Celeste
Martin

Shape Book

Trace and cut front and back covers in a thematic shape that corresponds to the writing your students are doing. You may want to use decorative paper or let students color the covers. Examples could be pumpkins for fall, trees for Arbor Day or Earth Day, etc. Help students determine the number of sheets of writing paper to include inside by estimating how much text they can fit on each page. Trace and cut the pages in the same thematic shape, using the covers as templates. Staple the cover and back to the writing pages.

Fact Book

Students should be given many opportunities to write about what they are learning in other curriculum areas. What better way to show off what they are learning than to produce a book of facts. For example, students may write a book called *Bear Facts*, designed to tell about the bears that they saw during the class trip to the zoo. Brainstorm with students to generate a list of possible topics and plan a mini-lesson to model how the book could be created. Students can create individual books, or each student can contribute a page to be bound into a class book.

Journal Writing

Most people who work with children know they always have something to say. Give students opportunities to practice expressing themselves with writing. This helps them begin to find their own writing voices and styles. Journal writing is an effective tool to help students explore writing with self-expression.

Journal writing is very personal writing. Students may write about pleasant times with family and friends, or they may release feelings of fear and sadness about events in their lives. No one should read a student's journal entry unless she gives permission. A willingness to share journal entries with others may develop if students trust that their rights to privacy will be respected if they choose not to share.

Students usually know what they want to write about, but they sometimes need help getting started. It is a good idea for the class to generate a list of journal topics. These topics can be displayed on chart paper in the room for students to reference, when needed. Possible journal topics include:

- my favorite foods
- best friends
- my best birthday
- playing a favorite game
- our family trip
- pets
- family
- my favorite holiday
- my house
- grandparents
- my favorite book

- my weekend
- a bad day I had
- an interesting person I know
- When I grow up . . .
- The best part about school is . . .
- a list of things I wonder about
- someone I admire
- I would like to learn how to . . .

Personal Picture Dictionary
(page 99)

Journal Bear Letter
(page 101)

Journal Page Templates
(page 105-107)

As you can see, with a little thought, the list of topics can be endless. And, so would the time spent grading them, if teachers graded them like other types of writing assignments! Fortunately, journals do not need to be corrected. Students should feel free to take risks when writing in their journals. Explain that a journal is not a place to have to worry about things like mechanics and correct spelling, but rather, it is a place to express worries, solve problems, set goals, tell stories, make lists, or anything else they want.

Making a Journal

There are many ways to make journals. Journals can be made so that they are durable enough to last a few days, weeks, or months. Here are some options.

- Fold a few sheets of lined or unlined paper and staple them in the center.
- Cut paper covers in the shape of a current classroom theme, then use the covers as templates to create inside pages. Staple the pages and covers together. See page 91 for examples of shape books.
- Use brads to attach writing paper in the center of folders. Have students decorate the fronts of the folders.
- Use a binding machine (available at copy shops) to attach pages of writing paper with plastic spiral binding. Bind blank pieces of construction paper to the fronts and backs to create more durable journals. Students can decorate the covers.

Journal Writing Mini-Lesson

As with any other type of writing, you need to model journal writing with students. Here is an example of how journal writing might be taught during a Writer's Workshop mini-lesson. (Refer to Chapter 1, page 16 for more in-depth information about Writer's Workshops.) The purpose for this mini-lesson is to model for students how to begin to make an entry in a journal. You will demonstrate selecting a topic and planning ideas before writing. You will need an overhead projector, chart paper, or chalkboard; transparency marker, pencil, chalk, or crayon; and journals (one writing booklet for each student).

Tell students, "A journal is a special book where you can write about anything that's on your mind. Each of you will have your own journal to write in. We will spend some time every week writing in our journals. You may share your journal writing with the class, if you want, but it will always be your choice. I will start a journal, too. I may not share my journal writing with you every time, but I will today so you can see how to write in your journal, or make a journal entry. I'll write today's date in the top right corner of my page because we always date our papers in this class. Hmm . . . what do I want to say today? I could write about. . . . "

Choose from your own ideas; these are simply examples. The important thing is to choose a topic that has meaning for you, so that students are encouraged to write about something meaningful to them. Then, write three ideas as you say them. "I could write about shopping with my children at the new comic book store, swimming in my neighbor's brand-new swimming pool, or learning to scuba dive for the first time"

Then, choose an idea. "I think I'll tell about swimming. I watched the contractors build this pool all summer, and since we are such good friends with our neighbors, we couldn't wait to go for a swim. Just a week ago, we finally did, and it was a lot of fun. Soon it will be too cold to swim, but we have a great summer to look forward to next year."

Next, move to the writing process. "Before I can write in paragraphs, I want to get my ideas down. I'll draw a picture and write a few ideas to help me remember what I want to say."

Draw a picture about your topic (see page 96 for an example). Since you gave a detailed talk to the class about why you chose the topic, try to be equally as detailed while you record your other thoughts. Write ideas and talk about what you are writing as you record your thoughts. As you jot down ideas, try to convey why this topic has meaning for you. It will sound something like, "The first thing that happened was my neighbor called me. Her name is Melissa, and she has two sons. She asked me to go swimming the next day. The weather surprised us and was sunny and warmer than we hoped. I put on my swimsuit and met the neighbors at the pool. Another kid from the neighborhood was there, too. The pool had tile around the edges, some new plants, and a table with an umbrella. We spent most of our time playing in the water and drinking lemonade." Continue to add details to the drawing and jot down words that will help you to write.

Then, move to writing complete sentences that are part of the actual entry. Say, "Now that I have my ideas, I can begin to write my journal entry." Write several sentences beneath the picture, reading each sentence to students as you write it. If you get "stuck," remind students that this is a journal, and you can cross out writing, change things, scribble out information, etc. Students will enjoy seeing this kind of freedom in your journal writing and will be encouraged to do the same.

Finally, read the entire entry to students. Encourage them to discuss it and ask questions. Add any details that students mention. You can even write their questions in your journal, and then encourage them to do the same when they read each other's journal entries later.

As you finish modeling the lesson, tell students, "You will have some time to write in your journals. Take a minute to think about three things you might want to write about. When I call your name, tell me the three things you are considering. List your three ideas in your journal, pick one to write about, draw a quick picture, and write some words to help you remember your thoughts. Then, write your sentences under your picture. You may look at my journal entry to help you remember what to do. Remember, this is your time to write about whatever you want." Leave your example up for students to reference during writing time.

After students observe your mini-lesson and understand your directions, let them begin to write in their personal journals. They can talk and share ideas, if they want. They can draw pictures and write their entries. Monitor and confer with individual students and small groups about their journal entries, providing encouragement when needed.

new pool   neighbors   nice weather   table
umbrella   plants   lemonade

Our neighbors have a new pool.

Our neighbors have two sons.

Yesterday was sunny and warm.

We put on our swimsuits and met our neighbors at
their new pool.

It has tile around the inside edge.

They have new plants and a table with an umbrella
and chairs.

You don't have to model only one kind of journal writing, although it is better to model one kind of writing at a time. You can show students many ways to use journals. Write a list of possible names for a new pet. Write about a problem you are having (nothing too personal) and brainstorm ways to solve it. Write drafts for friendly letters. Draw a plan for a garden you want to plant. In other words, use your journal as a forum for real writing you need to do. Give students as many options as you can think of and demonstrate.

Modeling Journal Writing

There are many different ways to use journals in your classroom besides those modeled here. Use the following ideas to inspire more journal writing.

Share Time

Ask for volunteers to share their writing. Students will begin to share when they are confident about their writing. Instruct other students to listen, question, and reflect about the journal entries.

The following student sample shows a journal entry from early in the year. The student followed the teacher's example. Once students are familiar with the process, they may choose whether to draw pictures and list key words before writing.

Personal Picture Dictionary

Before working with students, prepare a blank dictionary for each student. Make 26 copies of the template from page 99. Write one letter at the top of each page. Do not draw the corresponding pictures or write the sentences. That will be the students' task. Make one copy of each page for every student. You may choose to add construction paper covers for more durable dictionaries.

Next, show students samples of picture dictionaries and beginning dictionaries. Discuss how each is used. Explain that the pages are marked with the letters of the alphabet in order.

The next step is to give students the personal dictionaries. Ask students to turn to the page with a *p* at the top (or any letter you choose). Work as a class to model how to create a dictionary page. Tell students that the word penguin begins with *p*. Have everyone write the word *penguin* at the top of the first square on the page. Ask them to draw pictures of penguins, and write sentences about their penguins. Pictures and sentences will vary. Let them color the pictures. Have students generate a list of additional words beginning with *p* that can be illustrated on a dictionary page. Let each student choose three additional words to complete the *p* page of her dictionary. You may assign one page each day or allow students to work on their dictionaries during spare moments. Students may reference their dictionaries when writing.

Journal Writing — **PERSONAL PICTURE DICTIONARY**

Pp

penguin — Penguins can swim but cannot fly.

pet — My pet is a cat.

photograph — I brought home my school photograph.

police — Call the police in an emergency.

Journal Writing

PERSONAL PICTURE DICTIONARY

Journal Bear

An important goal of writing instruction is to encourage each student's love of writing. Ideally, students should learn to view writing as a positive activity. The journal bear activity provides a pleasant reason for writing. Introduce students to a stuffed animal with a name; for example, a bear named Freddie. Explain that Freddie has a journal that goes everywhere with him. Tell students that last week you took Freddie home and wrote several journal entries in the composition book to share with the class (make sure you write a few entries from Freddie's point of view before sharing, because students will want to see them). Read your entries to the class. Students will be hooked! They will realize that they get to have a "friend" go home with them, and they get to write about it and share with the class. Place student names in a jar and choose a student to take Freddie home for the weekend.

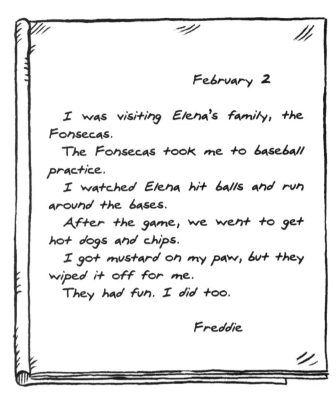

February 2

I was visiting Elena's family, the Fonsecas.
The Fonsecas took me to baseball practice.
I watched Elena hit balls and run around the bases.
After the game, we went to get hot dogs and chips.
I got mustard on my paw, but they wiped it off for me.
They had fun. I did too.

Freddie

Sample Journal Entry

Encourage students to write in the composition book about their adventures with Freddie.

Explain that the journal entry can be written from Freddie's point of view or the student's point of view. Students can also interview their parents for a different perspective. Each child gets a chance to enjoy the bear as he moves from family to family. The student who takes Freddie home for the weekend packs him in a special backpack you provide for easy travel. (You can also use a shopping bag with handles.) On Monday, have the student share with the class by reading the journal entry about his weekend adventures.

Brainstorm a list of rules for the use of the journal bear when he is away from class, such as no swimming or getting wet, keep him away from family pets, etc. Also state that you will take Freddie home when he is "sick" (needs minor repairs or a trip to the washing machine, or when a sick student has had him). The students can create a poster of rules to hang in the classroom for reference. In order to prepare parents for the assignment, use the template on page 101 to create a letter to send to parents with the journal bear when he goes home with a student. Add the agreed-upon rules to the letter.

_____
(date)

Dear Parents,

The purpose of this letter is to introduce our journal bear named Freddie. Your child has been selected to take Freddie home for a weekend visit with your family. He comes with a journal in which your child should write about the adventures of the weekend. The children are excited about this project!

Please return Freddie and the journal in the backpack on Monday. We will share Freddie's experiences with the class.

Below is a list of rules about things Freddie can't do while he is visiting for the weekend.

_____

_____

_____

_____

_____

Thank you for being a part of your child's writing experience.

Sincerely,

Process Journal

Keeping process journals is a method for students to record progress on a project. Students can use their journals to plan a project, write details as the project progresses, and record and reflect on the learning that has occurred. Students may keep individual, partner, or group journals, depending on how the work on the project is assigned. Allow each student to contribute frequently to the information in the process journal.

One possible way to use a process journal is to document each step of putting on a class play. You can use a different journal entry to document each step of the process, including writing or finding the script, choosing students to fulfill roles (actors, a director, props and costume managers, set designers, musicians, etc.), holding rehearsals, memorizing lines, building sets, finding props, advertising the play, holding a dress rehearsal, and performing. During the process, give students opportunities to write in their journals about how they feel the process is going, what they are learning, what they would do differently next time, etc.

You may choose to have one large class journal for students to use, or you may prefer to let students use their individual journals. If you have a group of actors, a group of scenery painters, etc., you may want to use one journal per group. These group journals can also be working journals in which students assign tasks, make lists of materials, set deadlines by which to have tasks completed, etc.

The other choice you have to make is how much to direct the journal writing. You may choose to give students freedom to write whatever they want in the journals, or you may decide to have them reply to specific prompts. You may also use some combination of the two. Use the examples on pages 103-104 to help you come up with your own ideas. Note: It is fun to use the What Did We Learn? section as a free-form autograph board at the end of the project (in this case, after the play performance). Use the Journal Page Border Templates (pages 105-107) to create your journal pages, if desired. If you want to eliminate the writing lines or add a calendar grid like the one on page 103, simply tape a piece of white paper over the writing lines on the template, then copy the template.

Mrs. Frank's Class Play

Who does what:

_____

Materials we need:

_____

PLANNING OUR PLAY

Title:
Characters:

Setting:

Plot:

PRACTICE SCHEDULE

Monday	Tuesday	Wednesday	Thursday	Friday

PERFORMING OUR PLAY

Cast members: _____

_____

_____

_____

_____

_____

Behind the scenes: _____

_____

_____

_____

_____

_____

_____

_____

_____

What Did We Learn? _____

REFLECTIONS ABOUT THE PLAY

What were the best things? _____

_____

_____

What would we change next time? _____

_____

_____

What did we learn? _____

_____

_____

_____

_____

_____

The Writing Teacher's Toolbox • CD-0354

Writing Conferences

Conferencing is a technique you can use to assess how writing is progressing and to help students focus on issues concerning individual pieces of writing. During conferences, students reflect on their writing and make positive changes to better communicate their ideas. Conferences are an important part of the writing process and may occur during any stage of writing. There are several types of conferences that will foster student self-learning.

Teacher Conferencing

Teacher conferencing happens when you meet with each student on a regular basis, as well as on an as-needed basis to discuss the effectiveness of her writing. There are some simple guidelines for conferencing that will help empower young writers.

- Even if you have already read it, ask the writer to read the piece of writing before you comment.
- Always be positive, patient, supportive, and respectful.
- Follow the writer's lead, letting her generate positive statements about what is going well in the writing, as well as concerns about areas that need improvement.
- Suggest ideas for consideration, but remember, it is important that the student maintains ownership of the writing.
- Keep it short, focusing on just one area of improvement per conference.

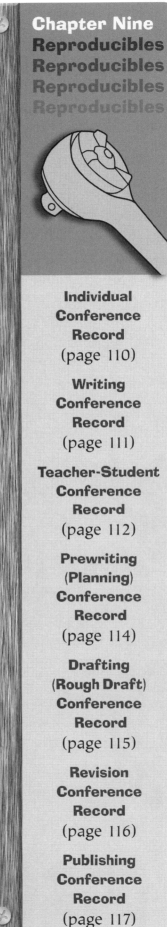

© Carson-Dellosa

Every conference will be different, but there are general questions and comments you can keep in mind to help students think about their writing. You will think of many others as you gain experience and confidence in your ability to conference with students about their writing.

- Tell me about your piece of writing.
- What part is your favorite? Why?
- Give me more details about this part.
- Have you stayed on topic?
- Can you tell me how you felt when this happened?
- Show me the part you think is the most exciting.
- Can you think of a better word to use for _____?
- Did you write things in the order that they happened?
- Why did you choose this topic?
- What will you do to make this piece of writing better?
- What do you mean in this part?
- How do you feel about the beginning? Ending? How can you rewrite the beginning or ending to show the reader more about how you feel?
- How are you creating a picture with words that the reader can understand?
- What do you need help with?
- What stage of the writing process are you in?
- Have you shared this with a friend? What were the suggestions for improvement?
- I like the way _____.

It is a good idea to document writing conferences much like you record anecdotal notes (page 36). Writing conferences help you assess progress and plan future instruction. Keeping conference records also allows you to note students who need to work on similar skills and to prepare small-group instruction to meet those needs. Many of the record-keeping ideas suggested for documenting anecdotal notes are appropriate for documenting conference activities as well. These records document student progress and are wonderful references during parent conferences. See pages 110-112 for templates of conference records.

Regardless of what type of conferencing you choose, it is possible to have several conferencing sheets for the same piece of writing as it moves through the stages of the writing process. Staple these sheets to the writing before it is included in the student's writing portfolio or folder.

Author's Name _____

Writing Conferences	INDIVIDUAL CONFERENCE RECORD		
Date	Type of Writing	Title/Topic	Comments

The Writing Teacher's Toolbox • CD-0354

Writing Conference Record
Writing Conference Record
Writing Conference Record

Author's Name _____

Date_____

Title_____

Focus of the conference: _____

_____

Comments: _____

_____

_____

_____

Writing Conference Record
Writing Conference Record
Writing Conference Record

Author's Name _____

Date_____

Title_____

Focus of the conference: _____

_____

Comments: _____

_____

_____

_____

Writing Conference Record
Writing Conference Record
Writing Conference Record

Author's Name _____

Date_____

Title_____

Focus of the conference: _____

_____

Comments: _____

_____

_____

_____

Author's Name _____

TEACHER-STUDENT CONFERENCE RECORD

Writing Conferences

Week of:	Monday	Tuesday	Wednesday	Thursday	Friday

The Writing Teacher's Toolbox • CD-0354

Self Conferencing

Self conferencing occurs when a student systematically reviews and considers the piece of writing before conferencing with you or peers. This is a good way for a student to consider what is going well and what concerns exist. This type of conferencing takes some practice, and the conference forms (pages 114-117) are more structured so that students find it to be a productive experience. You may want to model using the forms on one of your own pieces of writing.

Peer Conferencing

Peer conferencing takes place when two students pair up to be a reader and an author. The reader reads the author's work as the author listens. The reader says positive things about the writing (two stars). The reader asks questions and makes suggestions (a wish) to help improve the writing. The author makes the necessary changes. Many of the forms provided in Chapter 5 are appropriate for use in peer conferencing (pages 75, and 77-79).

Parent Conferencing

Informal parent conferencing happens when pieces of writing are sent home for parents to read. If you send writing home, include specific guidelines, such as asking parents to respond to the ideas rather than to mechanics and spelling. Ask parents to write comments on separate sheets of paper and return them for students to read. The students may share with the class if they want. This is an excellent way to encourage parent participation and to keep them updated regarding the student's writing progress. You may choose to date the responses and include them in the students' portfolios or writing folders as documentation of parental involvement. For more information about involving parents, see Chapter 10.

Whole-Class or Group Conferencing

Whole-class or group conferencing takes place only after a respectful environment has been created, procedures have been modeled, and goals have been established. Never display any student writing for discussion without the student's permission. Present writing on the overhead for the group to read. Have students respond to the writing either orally or in writing. Remind them to mention positive aspects before offering suggestions for improvement.

Name _____ Date _____

Title of Story _____

Writing Conferences	PREWRITING (PLANNING) CONFERENCE RECORD
Question	**Comments**
What are you going to write about?	_____ _____ _____ _____ _____
Who will be the audience?	_____ _____ _____ _____ _____
What is the most important thing you want to say?	_____ _____ _____ _____ _____

© Carson-Dellosa

The Writing Teacher's Toolbox • CD-0354

Name _____ Date _____

Title of Story _____

Writing Conferences — DRAFTING (ROUGH DRAFT) CONFERENCE RECORD

Question	Comments
How is the writing going?	_____ _____ _____ _____
What do you need help with?	_____ _____ _____ _____
What has surprised you in this writing?	_____ _____ _____ _____
What have you learned?	_____ _____ _____ _____

© Carson-Dellosa

Name _____ Date _____

Title of Story _____

REVISION CONFERENCE RECORD

Question	Comments
What can you do to make this piece better?	_____ _____ _____ _____
How does this draft sound when it is read aloud?	_____ _____ _____ _____
Do you have enough information? Do you have too much information? Why?	_____ _____ _____
Are you happy with your beginning and ending? If not, what would you change? Why?	_____ _____ _____

© Carson-Dellosa

Name _____ Date _____

Title of Story _____

PUBLISHING CONFERENCE RECORD

Question	Comments
How do you feel about this piece of writing?	_____ _____ _____
What part do you like best? Why?	_____ _____ _____
What was the reaction of your audience?	_____ _____ _____
How does this piece of writing compare to others you have written? Why?	_____ _____ _____

© Carson-Dellosa

Parental Involvement

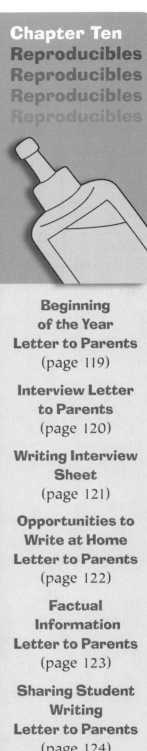

Parents are children's first teachers, and learning begins at home, long before children enter school. Children who have been encouraged to draw, scribble, and write at an early age develop confidence in writing and begin to develop writing skills. Even after parents send their children to school, they still play a key role in ensuring student success. Teachers can help students grow more effectively if parents are also supportive of teaching endeavors.

Parents should always feel welcome in the classroom, and should be informed regularly of class activities. You can use writing as a way to keep parents aware of what students are doing. In addition to having students complete individual writing assignments such as writing notes and letters home, sending home the journal bear (page 100), and having parent conferences (page 113), you, your students, and their parents can complete some of the assignments suggested in the sample letters in this chapter. Students can also compose a monthly newsletter to keep parents updated on what students are writing in the classroom. A newsletter can be a one-time event or can be sent home periodically during the school year.

If students have access to computers and software layout programs, you may want to let them help design letters, adding a school letterhead or their own class design. If you offer this option, save copies of each letter so that students can review their samples and see how their design skills improve throughout the year.

_____
(date)

Dear Parents,

This year, each student in our class will work to become a better writer. It is important for children to see parents as writers, too. We know people write for many reasons. Please let your child know when you write at home, and explain the purpose for your writing. (This includes making lists, drawing maps, writing directions, copying recipes, etc.) By sharing your writing experiences, you can help your child become a successful writer. Here are some ideas to get you started:

1. Let your child watch when you write, then let your child read your writing back to you.
2. Send occasional short, pleasant notes in your child's lunch box or backpack.
3. Encourage your child to write a shopping list or letters to friends or family members.
4. Let your child keep a date book or calendar.
5. In addition to telling favorite stories, write them down for your child to read again and again.
6. When reading to your child, occasionally point out the interesting parts and discuss why they caught your interest.
7. Discuss books, magazines, plays, or movies your child reads or views.

Thank you for your encouragement and support. Each month, we'll be sharing ideas to make writing fun for the whole family, and we would love to have you share your ideas, as well. Let's get started on a great year of writing!

Sincerely,

_____
(date)

Dear Parents,

Children learn to write by writing. Students need to learn to express themselves in writing, strengthen their confidence as writers, enjoy the process of writing, and understand that there are many purposes for writing.

I have interviewed your child about writing and recorded your child's answers on an attached sheet. The students in our class decided that it would be fun to interview their parents. Please help your child be successful with the interview your child has prepared for you. We will share our results as a class.

You are a valuable partner in your child's education. Thank you for helping with your child's writing.

Sincerely,

My Name _____ Date _____

Person Being Interviewed _____

Do you like to write? Why do you feel this way?

_____

_____

_____

_____

_____

What kinds of things do you write?

_____

_____

_____

_____

Tell about the first time you remember writing.

_____

_____

_____

_____

_____
(date)

Dear Parents,

Children need to have opportunities to write at home as well as at school. Children who are encouraged to write develop confidence in their writing abilities. Here are some tips to help motivate your child to develop good writing habits:

1. Read with your child every day. This increases vocabulary, gives a sense of story order, and helps your child understand that writing is a way of telling what you want to say.
2. Provide a comfortable place for your child to write. It should be a well lighted area and should be stocked with a variety of writing materials such as pencils, pens, markers, lined paper, unlined paper, and stationery.
3. Encourage your child to write frequently.
4. Create writing tasks with fun purposes. For example, ask your child to write three things that you need from the store that begin with the letter b. Or, have your child draw a map and label all of the places you must go to complete errands.
5. Listen to your child as he or she shares writing.
6. Praise your child for his or her writing efforts. Focus on positive aspects, not on errors.

These ideas will help develop the writer within your child. Thank you for your time and interest.

Sincerely,

_____
(date)

Dear Parents,

We are learning to write factual information. Students will be gathering information about their families in order to make factual books and graphs in class. Please help your child complete the following information sheet. You may help with spelling, but please let your child write the information on the sheet. Thank you for your help. We look forward to sharing our books and graphs with you.

Sincerely,

Family Information Sheet

There are _____ people in my family.

The names of the people in my family are _____

_____

There are _____ pets in my family.

The names of the pets in my family are _____

_____

Some of the things we do together are _____

_____

_____

_____

(date)

Dear Parents,

One night each week, students will choose pieces of their writing from their writing folders to share with family members. There will be a writing log attached to each piece for everyone who shares the writing to sign. There are also spaces for readers to make brief, positive comments.

We are considering content rather than mechanics of the pieces. Grammar, spelling, punctuation, and capitalization will be covered when we reach the editing stage of the writing process.

We will discuss the comments when the writing logs are returned the following day. The children are so excited to share their work with you. Thank you for being an important part of our writing process.

Sincerely,

Author's Name _____

Title of Story _____

Parental Involvement		WRITING LOG
Date	**Comment**	**Signature**

© Carson-Dellosa

_____
(date)

Dear Parents,

We are working to develop communication skills. We know that writing should have a purpose. You can help your child practice writing with a purpose by discussing the questions on the sheet below. Allow your child to write and discuss how he or she feels about the activities we did this week. It is a great opportunity to find out what your child is doing in school.

Thank you so much for your help!

Sincerely,

Looking Back on the Week

My Name _____ Date _____

Some things we did _____

_____

The part I liked best this week _____

_____

I still don't understand _____

_____

I would like to _____

_____

Authors' Tea
Authors' Tea
Authors' Tea

Dear Parents,

Come join us for an Authors' Tea! We want to share our stories with you.

Where? _____

When? _____

Who? _our class authors_____

The students will read their published work. Refreshments will be served. Please join us for this fun event.

Sincerely,

Authors' Tea
Authors' Tea
Authors' Tea

Dear Parents,

Come join us for an Authors' Tea! We want to share our stories with you.

Where? _____

When? _____

Who? _our class authors_____

The students will read their published work. Refreshments will be served. Please join us for this fun event.

Sincerely,

Bibliography

Calkins, Lucy McCormick. *The Art of Teaching Writing.* 2d ed. Portsmouth: Heinemann, 1994.

Calkins, Lucy McCormick and Donna Santman. *Management of a Writing Workshop.* Summary. Teachers College Writing Project. New York: Columbia University, 1997.

Graves, Donald H. *A Fresh Look at Writing.* Portsmouth: Heinemann, 1994.

Routman, Regie. *Invitations: Changing as Teachers and Learners in K–12.* Portsmouth: Heinemann, 1991.